**GOOD
HOUSEKEEPING**

28-DAY
MEDITERRANEAN
DIET

GOOD HOUSEKEEPING

28-DAY MEDITERRANEAN DIET

DAILY MEAL PLANS, DELICIOUS RECIPES & EXPERT TIPS

Stefani Sassos, MS, RDN, CDN
Registered Dietitian, Good Housekeeping Institute

Kate Merker, Chief Food Director, Good Housekeeping

© 2021 by Hearst Magazine Media, Inc.

COVER PHOTOGRAPHY
Mike Garten

INTERIOR PHOTOGRAPHY
Natasha Breen: 13; Ted Cavanaugh: 129; EasyBuy4u: 9; Eternity in an Instant: 20; fcafotodigital: 31; Mike Garten: 44, 49, 51-55, 59-76, 89-96, 99-101, 105-115, 133, 137, 141, 149-151, 155, 169, 173-183; Pernille Loof: 143; nata_zhekova: 26; Danielle Occhiogrossos Daly: 43, 57, 61-65, 103, 111, 117, 131, 135, 139, 145-147, 153, 157, 185-197; Con Poulos: 47, 171; Kat Teusch: 45; The Noun Project: 24-25; Claudia Totir: 13; Kristina Vianello: 23; VICUSCHKA: 17; Westend61: 14, 19

Book design by Michael Wilson

Recipes by Erika Dugan, Kate Merker, Kristina Kurek, Taylor Murray, and Cybelle Tondu

Library of Congress Cataloging-in-Publication Data is on file with the publisher.

ISBN 978-1-950099-93-1

Printed in China

2 4 6 8 10 9 7 5 3 paperback

HEARST

INTRODUCTION

Growing up in a Greek-American family, Mediterranean foods were at the forefront of all our meals and traditions. Not only did these incredible foods burst with flavor and vibrancy, but they also made healthy eating enjoyable and sustainable.

That may be why the Mediterranean diet, inspired by healthy communities in nations like Greece, Spain, France and Italy, is consistently ranked as the best diet year after year. Snagging the top spot in *U.S. News and World Report*'s annual diet ranking for the fourth year in a row, this lifestyle-based diet comes with the least amount of rules and focuses on abundance rather than restriction.

In putting this plan together with the help of culinary experts in Good *Housekeeping*'s Test Kitchen, I was able to take inspiration from my roots and design a plan that not only allows you to prepare delicious meals, but also to eat for longevity and good health. Whether you're following this plan to lose weight or to get some culinary inspiration, you'll find each day to be packed with exciting easy-to-make recipes that you'll look forward to eating and will help you feel your best.

Stefani Sassos, MS, RDN, CDN
Registered Dietitian, Good Housekeeping Institute

CONTENTS

RECIPES

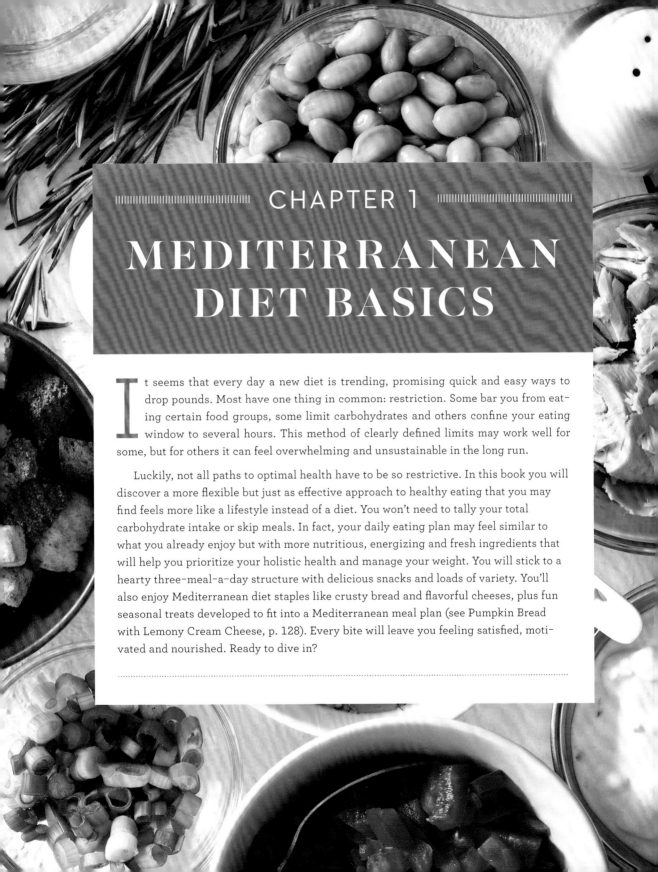

CHAPTER 1
MEDITERRANEAN DIET BASICS

I t seems that every day a new diet is trending, promising quick and easy ways to drop pounds. Most have one thing in common: restriction. Some bar you from eating certain food groups, some limit carbohydrates and others confine your eating window to several hours. This method of clearly defined limits may work well for some, but for others it can feel overwhelming and unsustainable in the long run.

Luckily, not all paths to optimal health have to be so restrictive. In this book you will discover a more flexible but just as effective approach to healthy eating that you may find feels more like a lifestyle instead of a diet. You won't need to tally your total carbohydrate intake or skip meals. In fact, your daily eating plan may feel similar to what you already enjoy but with more nutritious, energizing and fresh ingredients that will help you prioritize your holistic health and manage your weight. You will stick to a hearty three-meal-a-day structure with delicious snacks and loads of variety. You'll also enjoy Mediterranean diet staples like crusty bread and flavorful cheeses, plus fun seasonal treats developed to fit into a Mediterranean meal plan (see Pumpkin Bread with Lemony Cream Cheese, p. 128). Every bite will leave you feeling satisfied, motivated and nourished. Ready to dive in?

WHAT IS THE MEDITERRANEAN DIET?

While other diets are often quite specific, requiring you to meticulously track macronutrients and your timing of meals, the Mediterranean diet can seem less structured. That's because it's more a way of eating than it is a strict weight-loss program. Think of the Mediterranean diet as a lifestyle inspired by cultures in Greece, Spain, Italy and France, among others. It's an approach to cooking that emphasizes vegetables, naturally leading to a ton of antioxidants, vitamins and minerals in your diet.

Unlike quick-fix fad diets, the Mediterranean way of eating doesn't require you to completely cut out any of your favorites (yes, red wine is included in moderation!). The diet is rich in produce, whole grains and lean protein, supplying antioxidants and heart-healthy unsaturated fats (think: olive oil rather than butter). You'll find that those following the Mediterranean diet enjoy plenty of fatty fish (especially salmon, which is considered a staple) alongside whole-grain sides like farro, plenty of crisp vegetables and an abundance of supercharged legumes, nuts and seeds.

The Mediterranean lifestyle quickly rose to fame among doctors back in 2013 after a team at the University of Barcelona studied more than 7,000 participants who drastically improved their heart health after adopting the diet. The scientific evidence of the diet's effectiveness has piled up since then; a study published in the *The BMJ* journal found that elderly individuals may vastly improve brain function and their own longevity by adopting the Mediterranean diet. Evidence suggests that this dietary routine can fight inflammation as we age, stopping the production of chemicals in the body that are known to contribute to cognitive decline. Plus, the diet may also prevent chronic diseases such as diabetes. It's no wonder that Ikaria, an island in Greece, has been designated as one of the five Blue Zones of the world where people live the longest.

DIET VS. LIFESTYLE

One of the biggest reasons the Mediterranean diet is so different from other weight-loss methods is that it is less of a diet and more of a lifestyle. Many traditional diets are limited and extreme, which makes them doable for just the short-term. For many people, this is easy to stick with for a couple of days or weeks, but once the diet is completed it is tempting to revert back to old habits, potentially undoing any of the progress made during the program.

A lifestyle approach to healthy living doesn't have an end date. But that doesn't mean you will never get to eat your favorite foods again. It means this plan is built to be flexible and sustainable, but most importantly it includes benefits beyond the number on the scale. The Mediterranean eating plan we've created here will leave you feeling energized, satisfied and excited about your next meal, so keeping up with it long past the 28 days will feel natural. Another bonus of a lifestyle approach? You'll keep reaping its benefits — from weight loss to improved energy — for as long as you stick with it.

MEDITERRANEAN DIET STAPLES

Powerful Proteins
- Beans
- Eggs
- Feta & Goat Cheese
- Fish
- Greek Yogurt
- Lentils
- Poultry

Antioxidant-Rich Produce
- Apricots
- Artichokes
- Bell Peppers
- Berries
- Broccoli
- Carrots
- Cherries
- Eggplant
- Dark Leafy Greens
- Peaches
- Potatoes & Root Vegetables
- Zucchini

Hearty Grains
- Barley
- Bulgar Wheat
- Farro
- Oats
- Quinoa
- Whole-Grain Bread

Healthy Fats
- Avocado
- Extra Virgin Olive Oil
- Nuts & Seeds
- Olives

THE MEDITERRANEAN KITCHEN

A Mediterranean kitchen is packed with fresh produce, lean proteins, seafood and healthy fats. Here are some delicious ingredients that you might find useful when stocking your kitchen to add Mediterranean flavor and flare at every meal.

HERBS & SPICES

- Allspice
- Basil
- Bay Leaves
- Cinnamon
- Cloves
- Coriander
- Crushed Red Pepper Flakes
- Cumin
- Dill Weed
- Garlic Powder
- Mint
- Nutmeg
- Onion Powder
- Oregano
- Parsley
- Rosemary
- Sage
- Smoked Paprika
- Sumac
- Thyme
- Turmeric
- Za'atar

OILS & VINEGARS

- Apple Cider Vinegar
- Balsamic Vinegar
- Extra Virgin Olive Oil
- Red Wine Vinegar

LEGUMES, NUTS & GRAINS

- Almonds
- Barley
- Buckwheat
- Bulgur Wheat
- Cannellini Beans
- Chickpeas
- Couscous
- Farro
- Fava Beans
- Kidney Beans
- Lentils (Red, Yellow and Green)
- Navy Beans
- Oats
- Orzo
- Pine Nuts
- Pistachios
- Quinoa
- Walnuts
- Yellow Split Peas

OTHER ESSENTIALS

- Olives
- Sesame Seeds
- Tahini
- Tomatoes & Diced Tomatoes
- Dry Red & White Wine

4 WAYS THE MEDITERRANEAN DIET IS UNLIKE ANY OTHER

The Mediterranean style of eating is less of a diet and more of a way of life. It doesn't focus on restrictions, counting calories or measuring portions (snooze!). Instead, it emphasizes filling up on a wide variety of whole, nutrient-dense foods and taking the time to savor every last bite. This is what makes it such a successful method for weight management and warding off chronic disease. Because a Mediterranean-style plan is so flexible, you won't be craving a return to your old way of eating once the 28 days are complete. Instead, you'll have a whole new outlook on the food you eat and how good food nourishes you. Here's what else makes this plan so unique:

1. You'll indulge every day. You'll enjoy delicious, quality foods, like flavorful cheeses and hearty grains. Because you'll regularly enjoy foods that are often restricted on other diets (think carbohydrates and healthy fats), you'll be less likely to feel the impulse to overindulge.

2. Every meal will feel like a celebration. A Mediterranean-style diet is centered on enjoying meals with loved ones. This adds a dimension to mealtime other than food, one that encourages you to focus more on who's at the table rather than what's on it. To help you focus on the importance of shared experiences and overall wellness, we've included space in the daily meal plan for you to note how you connected with others.

3. You'll move the way you want to. The Mediterranean lifestyle involves plenty of physical activity and daily movement. By engaging in the types of exercise you love, you'll establish healthy habits that'll stick with you for life. Remember: ALL MOVEMENT IS GOOD MOVEMENT! Use the Movement field of the plan to track your daily physical activity, whether it's a high-intensity workout class or a stroll around the neighborhood with friends.

4. You'll see food in a whole new way. This way of life emphasizes the holistic experience of growing, eating and enjoying food. You'll view your meals as more than sustenance. You'll eat every bite more mindfully, with a deeper understanding of the time and energy involved in producing the food on your plate.

CHAPTER 2

HOW TO STICK TO THE PLAN

Because the Mediterranean diet doesn't require meticulous tracking of calories, fat, carbohydrates or any nutrient, you may find it's easier to follow than other plans. Of course, any new way of eating requires some adjustment. On this plan, you won't have to overhaul your kitchen or radically change your existing habits. All you need to do is make little shifts to what you're already doing. Here are essential tips to ensure your success on the plan and help you stick with it in the long run.

PREPARE YOUR KITCHEN

You're more likely to make healthy choices when you have nutritious and delicious ingredients at the ready in your kitchen. So, start this plan by making sure there are plenty of Mediterranean-friendly ingredients waiting for you every time you open your fridge. Follow the shopping lists for each week of the meal plan so you have everything you need to make the recipes in this book. You will also want to have a constant stock of the Mediterranean kitchen staples from pages 12 and 13 on hand so you can create amazing flavorful dishes on the fly and keep your kitchen armed with healthy choices that inspire you to stay consistent. We also suggest stocking up on meal prep tools, such as airtight containers, so you can prep as much of the weekly plans ahead of time as possible.

PLAN WHERE YOU WILL EAT

Ensuring success on this plan starts with thinking about where you will eat, not just what you will eat. Your routine, and the environments it puts you in, is crucial in determining what types of foods are available to you. Think of where you end up eating your meals and snacks throughout the week. If it's often at your desk during 10 free minutes before your next meeting, prepping much of your meal in advance will help you avoid succumbing to the convenience of other less healthy options.

ALWAYS PACK A SNACK

People, places and activities often seem like they pop out of nowhere, sidetracking your previous plans for a health-promoting activity or meal. Plan for the unplanned by keeping a portable snack with you at all times. If a meeting runs late or you won't be able to make it home in time for dinner, at least you have a healthy option to tide you over. Roasted crunchy chickpeas or homemade trail mix are easy go-tos that you can stash in your bag or desk at work that won't spoil.

EAT MINDFULLY

This plan is brimming with fresh, flavor-packed ingredients. When you eat too quickly or while scrolling on your phone, you might miss the whole experience and find yourself feeling less satisfied with your meal. Use these tips to stay in the moment at every meal:

AIM TO MAKE MEALS LAST FOR 20 MINUTES

Take time to chew your food, savor the flavors and appreciate each bite. If you find that you're still going very fast, try to set your fork down after every few bites. It takes about 20 minutes for your stomach to signal to your brain that it's full. Give yourself time to digest the meal and get in tune with satiety, the feeling of fullness and satisfaction that you get from eating.

CHECK IN WITH YOURSELF BEFORE EATING

Start with examining your hunger and appetite. Hunger is your physiological need for food, whereas appetite is your desire for food. Try to examine how your body is feeling at the beginning of a meal; are you eating out of boredom or anxiety? Conversely, have you let your body go too long without food? Slight hunger is okay but anything more severe can make it difficult to slow down and eat mindfully. Commit to incorporating balanced meals throughout the day so you have an appetite at mealtimes but aren't ravenous.

GIVE EVERY BITE 100% OF YOUR ATTENTION

In order to fully immerse yourself, it's important to disconnect from electronics and major distractions. Silence your phone, turn off the TV and sit down at the kitchen table so you are fully present in the meal.

START WITH THE RIGHT MINDSET

A positive outlook can make all the difference when it comes to staying on track. Head into this plan knowing that you are capable of sticking with it for 28 days, come good days *and* bad. We've included space for you to track your mood throughout the entire process so you can see how your headspace is connected to your commitment. When a rough day comes around, remember the confidence you felt today and move on with the same optimism.

MEDITERRANEAN DIET SNACKS

Incorporate any of these simple Mediterranean-inspired snacks into your meal plan. Each one is 200 calories or less.

- 1 small apple + 1 Tbsp natural almond butter
- 10 carrot sticks + 2 Tbsp hummus
- 3 cups air-popped popcorn + 2 Tbsp shredded Parmesan cheese
- 1 cup lentil soup
- ½ whole-wheat pita dipped in ¼ cup tzatziki
- 100-calorie toasted English muffin + 2 Tbsp low-fat cream cheese
- 10 pita chips + ½ cup fresh bruschetta
- ½ avocado drizzled with lemon or lime juice, sea salt and pepper
- ½ cup dry-roasted chickpeas
- ¼ trail mix with raw nuts, seeds and dried fruit
- ½ cup low-fat ricotta cheese + 1 chopped fresh tomato + 1 Tbsp fresh chopped basil
- ¼ cup walnuts
- 1 cup vegetable soup
- 1 hard-boiled egg + 2 Tbsp roasted pistachios
- 5 whole-grain crackers + 1 oz feta cheese
- ½ cup low-fat cottage cheese + 1 cup orange slices
- 2 large hard-boiled eggs with salt and pepper
- 1 small sliced pear topped with 1 oz goat cheese and drizzle honey
- 2 celery stalks + 2 Tbsp natural peanut butter
- 2 Tbsp almonds + 1 square dark chocolate

CHAPTER 3

HOW THE PLAN WORKS

E very element of this plan is created to help you seamlessly adopt a Mediterranean way of eating into your life as it is today. Because a Mediterranean diet is less about counting numbers and more about dialing in to how food makes you feel, the 28-day plan does not include detailed breakdowns of calories, fat or carbohydrates. Each day of the plan is portioned to hit around 1,500 calories, which is a good target for most people aiming to lose weight safely. Feel free to add more food to this plan for weight maintenance, such as an extra snack or daily dessert. If you're not sure what the appropriate amount of calories is for you, consult with your physician or registered dietitian.

You'll also find that the plan is designed to limit the amount of work you need to put into each meal. Recipes that can be prepped ahead of time are marked with a ⏰. These can be made up to two days ahead of when you are scheduled to eat them. Many meals are portioned for 4 servings so you can easily share these wholesome dishes with your family. If you are cooking for yourself, the multiple servings allow you to get a jumpstart on future meals. Simply freeze the leftovers and enjoy when you need a quick meal. Most recipes can be easily halved should you wish to. Unless otherwise noted, eat 1 serving.

FAQS

Does it matter what brand of food I buy?
This plan calls for various store-bought packaged goods, such as flavored Greek yogurt and pita. When purchasing these, always remember: The fewer the ingredients, the better. Plus, ingredient lists go by weight, so check to see if the first ingredient is a whole real food. Feel free to buy whatever brand you prefer, just keep an eye out for added sugar. Aim to purchase items like Greek yogurt or granola that have no more than 8 grams added sugar per serving.

Can I drink alcohol on this plan?
A Mediterranean diet customarily allows red wine in moderation, but it's important to speak with your doctor before incorporating this into the plan. Drinking in moderation means one drink a day or less for women and two drinks a day or less for men. One drink is equivalent to about 5 oz of wine. There are certain situations, such as if you are on a medication that interacts with alcohol or you are recovering from an alcohol use disorder, in which alcohol should be avoided altogether.

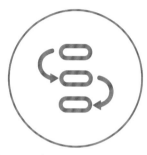

Can I make ingredient swaps based on taste or dietary restriction?
Most grains in this plan can be substituted with gluten-free options if needed, such as brown rice and quinoa. Regular breads can easily be swapped out for gluten-free breads; just look for varieties that are minimally processed, if possible.

If you are vegetarian, the plan includes several plant-powered meals, and produce is abundant in this program. But for certain recipes that utilize chicken or beef, you can experiment with vegan protein sources like tofu and tempeh instead. Beans and lentils, cornerstones of the Mediterranean diet, are also great protein swaps.

If you follow a dairy-free diet, a plain yogurt alternative can work in place of Greek yogurt at most snacks and meals. Certain brands now offer cheese alternatives made from cashews and chickpeas that would work well to substitute cheese in most recipes.

Should I eat my meals at a certain time?

The best times to eat are dictated by your own body! Practice listening to your body and becoming more familiar with your hunger cues. A good rule of thumb is to eat something every three to four hours during the day, because going too long without food may cause you to feel ravenous and reach for a quick fix. Even if you aren't hungry in the morning, listening to your body also involves knowing that if you don't eat at breakfast, you may feel extremely hungry or fatigued later on. Tuning in to your body is about making sure you are adequately nourished and checking in with cues like mood and energy levels too.

How can I incorporate dining out into this lifestyle after the 28 days?

Prioritize plant-based meals when possible at restaurants, placing an emphasis on tons of fresh produce. Always incorporate a salad, vegetable-based soup or produce-powered side dish with any meal. Look for terms on the menu that indicate healthier preparation methods like "baked," "steamed," "roasted," "broiled," "grilled," "poached," "seared" and "lightly sautéed." On the other hand, try to avoid or limit choosing dishes that say "smothered," "heavy," "rich," "creamy," "crunch," "tempura" or "crispy."

What should I do if I miss a day?

Don't sweat it, you're only human! Get right back on track with the plan and resume with the next day. There is no need to resort to detox methods or extreme restriction after a slipup; just get back to the plan and recommit as best you can.

HOW TO STORE LEFTOVERS

Most leftovers can be refrigerated in airtight containers between
two and five days depending on what they are. But there are a few things you can do to make
them last longer and taste better the second time around.

Store Separately:
Meats and vegetables not only reheat at different rates, but you also may want to use them for different meals in upcoming days. Storing them separately helps maintain optimal fresh-ness and gives you additional meal planning flexibility.

Keep it Whole:
If you cook steak, pork or chicken and the recipe calls for slicing it, but you know you are not going to eat it all, it is better to keep it whole. It is less likely to dry out, especially if you plan on reheating it.

Wait to Dress and Top:
Instead of tossing or topping with vinaigrettes, tender herbs and greens or crunchy nuts, leave them out and store separately. Drizzle, fold in, sprinkle and add just before serving.

ELEMENTS OF THE MEAL PLAN

We've designed this plan to be as effortless as possible to follow, providing resources and tools to help you navigate some of the most common obstacles to sticking with any eating plan. Here's exactly what you will find and how to best use it:

WEEK AT-A-GLANCE

At the beginning of each week of the plan you will see every meal and snack you will be eating for those seven days. Take a moment before each week to review the list. Note any ingredients or complete meals you can prep ahead and on what days. Identify the dishes that need to be made fresh and plan accordingly. If you are planning on using any substitute ingredients (see p. 24), be sure to add those to your shopping list for the week.

WEEKLY SHOPPING LIST

Nothing derails a diet faster than realizing you're missing an essential ingredient. Our comprehensive shopping lists ensure you have everything you need on hand and in the correct quantity for every breakfast, lunch, dinner and snack for the week. Snap a photo and reference it on your grocery run.

DAILY MENUS

On each day of the plan you will find exactly what you will be eating that day. In addition to your daily menu, we've also included space for you to track five essential elements of overall wellness, plus some handy space to jot down notes, such as your favorite meal of the day. These five elements are:

WATER

No matter what type of eating plan you adopt, staying hydrated is important to keeping your body happy and healthy. It's easy to confuse your need for water with hunger, so knowing how much you need each day is essential. A reasonable goal for the average person is about eight cups per day, which is what we will give you as a benchmark. For a more accurate hydration estimate, try to drink ½ oz of water for each pound you weigh. If you weigh 160 lbs, this will equal 80 oz of water, or 10 cups.

Aim to reach your daily hydration goals primarily with water, but you can also sip on sparkling water, unsweetened coffee and tea or fruit-infused water. Aside from drinking your way to your individualized daily water requirements, you can (and should!) also consume high-water-content foods like cucumbers, tomatoes, watermelon, asparagus, grapes and celery. They'll hydrate you and keep you full due to their higher fiber content.

MOVEMENT/WORKOUT

Regular exercise is vital to any health regimen, but it's important to understand the value of all types of movement, not just what happens in the gym. Activities that don't fit the standard workout bucket, like spending 30 minutes raking leaves or a couple hours walking the mall, still count as physical activity. Tracking such movement may help motivate you to do even more in addition to your weekly workout class of choice. Always consult with your physician or health care practitioner before starting any exercise regimen.

The American Heart Association recommends 150 minutes of moderate intensity aerobic activity or 75 minutes of vigorous intensity aerobic activity, or a combination of both, preferably spread throughout the week. This plan will give you space to note the type of activity you performed, how long you did it for and the intensity at which you did it. For a mood-booster, review your log at the end of the week. You may find that you did more than you thought!

SLEEP

Quality shut-eye is a critical component of your ability to stick with any health plan. When you're tired, you're more likely to cave to cravings, lose focus on your goals and make food decisions you wouldn't otherwise consider. Research published in the journal *Sleep* found that people with restricted sleep had altered levels of endocannabinoids, one of the chemical signals that affects appetite and the brain's reward system. Lack of sleep may also leave you too tired to get in the quality movement you need for overall wellness and keep you from engaging in social activities (which have their own weight-loss benefits!). Keep an eye on how sleep is impacting your waking life by tracking your bedtime and wake-up time each day. Note if it affected your cravings or ability to stick with the plan.

MOOD

A stressful day at work, an unexpected bill or just a gloomy Monday has the potential to influence your eating decisions. Less-than-perfect moods are part of life, so being aware of them is a productive step to not letting them get the best of you. Use the mood tracker to identify your general mood for the day and make a few notes about what might have caused it, how it did or didn't impact your plan or ideas for how to handle things next time.

CONNECTION

Relationships with others is a key piece of the Mediterranean lifestyle. Meals are often seen as opportunities to share time with friends and family, shifting the focus from food to connection. When you bring this same attention to eating as a shared experience, you will likely find that you eat more slowly — after all, it's hard to hurry through a meal when you're holding an engaging conversation! This gives you time to tune into your satiety signals instead of quickly polishing off your plate. To help you make this a priority during these 28 days, we've included space for you to write down how you connected with others that day. It can take the form of a shared meal or simply a phone call with a friend after work.

BONUS TRACKER PAGES

At the end of the meal plan you will find extra pages to track the above details plus space to create your own daily menus. Remember, the Mediterranean diet is a lifestyle. It doesn't need to end once you complete the 28 days. Use this area of the book to start building your own meal plan using the recipes you loved most from the first four weeks. By the end you should have enough daily menus to inspire your meals for months to come!

BEFORE YOU BEGIN

Complete this page to get a sense of where you are starting and to set goals for the next 28 days. Refer back to it whenever you need a boost of confidence and to see how far you've come!

DATE: _____

I AM STARTING THIS PLAN BECAUSE _____
_____
_____
_____

AT THE END OF THIS PLAN I WANT TO FEEL _____
_____
_____
_____

MY CURRENT WATER INTAKE IS USUALLY _____
_____
_____
_____

MY CURRENT MOVEMENT IS USUALLY _____
_____
_____
_____

MY CURRENT SLEEP IS USUALLY _____
_____
_____
_____

MY CURRENT MOOD IS USUALLY _____
_____
_____
_____

MY CURRENT CONNECTION IS USUALLY _____
_____
_____
_____

CHAPTER 4

THE MEAL PLAN

MEAL PLAN STAPLES

Keep these ingredients on hand while completing the meal plan.

- Olive oil
- Kosher salt
- Black pepper
- Chili powder
- Paprika
- Ground cumin

- Ground coriander
- Crushed red pepper
- Cayenne
- Dried oregano
- Low-sodium soy sauce
- All-purpose flour
- Whole-wheat flour

- Baking powder
- Baking soda
- Granulated sugar
- Brown sugar
- Ground cinnamon
- Pure vanilla extract

WEEK 1 At-a-Glance

DAY 1

BREAKFAST
🕐 Spinach and Pepper Mini Frittatas + 2 Slices Sprouted Grain Bread

LUNCH
🕐 Roasted Tomato Soup with Parmesan Crostini

DINNER
Seared Salmon with Lentil Salad

SNACK
Honey-Blueberry Oats

DAY 2

BREAKFAST
🕐 Vegan Coconut Chia Pudding

LUNCH
🕐 Greek Salad + 4 oz Grilled Chicken Breast

DINNER
Pork Tenderloin with Quinoa Pilaf

SNACK
🕐 Best-Ever Spinach Artichoke Dip + 10 Pita Chips

DAY 3

BREAKFAST
🕐 No-Bake Fruit and Nut Bars

LUNCH
Citrusy Shrimp-Stuffed Avocados

DINNER
Pan-Fried Chicken with Lemony Roasted Broccoli + 1 cup Cooked Quinoa Pilaf (Premade or Leftover)

SNACK
1 5.3-oz Container Low-Sugar Flavored Greek Yogurt

DAY 4

BREAKFAST
🕐 Vegan Coconut Chia Pudding

LUNCH
Whole-Grain Pita with Leftover Pan-Fried Chicken & 🕐 Spinach Artichoke Dip

DINNER
🕐 Roasted Squash and Couscous Salad

SNACK
1 cup Fresh-Cut Vegetable Crudité

DAY 5

BREAKFAST
Blueberry-Banana-Nut Smoothie

LUNCH
🕐 White Bean and Tuna Salad with Basil Vinaigrette + 10 Pita Chips

DINNER
🕐 Mini Meatballs with Garlicky Tomatoes

SNACKS
🕐 No-Bake Fruit and Nut Bar 2 Squares 70% Dark Chocolate

DAY 6

BREAKFAST
🕐 Shakshuka + 2 Slices Sprouted Grain Bread

LUNCH
🕐 Grilled Halloumi Salad

DINNER
Fennel Roasted Chicken and Peppers + 1 Large Sweet Potato with 1 Tbsp Butter, Sea Salt and Pepper

SNACK
½ cup Crunchy Chickpea Snacks

DAY 7

BREAKFAST
🕐 Orange and Pear Bran Muffin + 1 5.3-oz Container Low-Sugar Flavored Greek Yogurt

LUNCH
🕐 Butternut Squash White Bean Soup

DINNER
Shrimp and Zoodles Sheet Pan Dinner

SNACK
1 cup Lightly Salted Pistachios with Shells

PRODUCE

Veggies

3 heads garlic
2½ small red onions
2 yellow onions
1½ shallots
1 large sweet potato
1 medium (about 2¼ lbs) butternut squash
1 large butternut squash
1 1-in. piece fresh ginger
1½ lbs spiralized zucchini
1½ lbs broccoli
12 oz green beans
8 oz asparagus
4 oz snap peas
1 small seedless cucumber
2 Persian cucumbers
3 bell peppers (red, yellow and orange)
1 large red pepper
1 small red chile
½ serrano chile
3¾ lbs tomatoes
1½ lbs cherry and/or grape tomatoes
1 lb Campari tomatoes
1 ripe avocado
1 cup fresh vegetable crudités

Greens & Lettuce

4 cups torn lettuce
5 5-oz pkgs. baby spinach
4 cups baby arugula
9 scallions (2 bunches)

Herbs

¼ cup flat-leaf parsley
½ cup cilantro
1 cup lightly packed basil leaves
½ cup dill
7 sprigs thyme
1 tsp fresh oregano

Fruit

6 lemons
2 limes
1 orange
½ cup blueberries
¼ cup berries
½ cup pomegranate seeds
1 medium red pear
1 banana

MEAT & SEAFOOD

4 6-oz boneless, skinless chicken breasts
4 oz grilled chicken
4 small chicken legs (about 2 lbs)
1 lb ground beef
2 small (about ¾ lb each) pork tenderloins
4 5-oz skinless salmon fillets
½ lb cooked shrimp
20 large peeled and deveined shrimp

REFRIGERATED & DAIRY

1 Tbsp unsalted butter
20 large eggs
1½ cups 1% milk
2 cups almond milk
½ cup buttermilk
2 5.3-oz containers low-sugar flavored Greek yogurt
1½ Tbsp sour cream
8 oz feta cheese
3 oz Parmesan (about ¾ cup grated)
4½ oz Halloumi cheese
3 Tbsp fresh goat cheese
2 oz pecorino cheese

FROZEN

½ cup frozen blueberries

BREAD & BAKERY

2 slices sprouted grain bread
4 ½-in.-thick slices baguette
1 whole-grain pita

PANTRY

Oils, Vinegars, Condiments & Spices

4 Tbsp red wine vinegar
2 Tbsp balsamic vinegar
2 Tbsp white wine vinegar
4 tsp Dijon mustard
2 Tbsp mayonnaise
2 5-oz cans solid white tuna in water
1 Tbsp fennel seeds

Grains

2½ cups pearl couscous
2 cups quinoa
½ cup couscous
6 cups low-sodium chicken broth
¼ cup panko
1 cup old-fashioned rolled oats

Beans & Veggies

2 15-oz cans cannellini beans
1 15-oz cans chickpeas
1 15-oz can small white beans
1 15-oz can lentils

1 14-oz can artichoke hearts
2 Tbsp capers
⅓ cup pitted Kalamata olives

Broth & Wine

2 Tbsp dry white wine

Baking

1 cup whole-wheat flour
2 tsp confectioners' sugar
⅓ cup honey
3 Tbsp agave syrup
1 cup wheat bran
2 squares 70% dark chocolate
1 14-oz can coconut milk

Nuts, Seeds & Fruits

1 cup roasted almonds
½ cup blanched almonds
¼ cup roasted pistachios
1 cup lightly salted pistachios with shells
¾ cup pepitas
½ cup black chia seeds
¾ cup dried fruit
¼ cup dried apricots
1 cup (about 12) pitted dates
¼ cup almond butter
2 Tbsp peanut or almond butter
2 Tbsp orange marmalade
¼ cup unsweetened applesauce

Chips

10 pita chips
¾ cup sweet potato chips
½ cup crunchy chickpea snacks

DAY 1

BREAKFAST
Spinach and Pepper Mini
Frittatas (2 Servings) (p. 42) +
2 Slices Sprouted
Grain Bread

LUNCH
Roasted Tomato Soup with
Parmesan Crostini
(2 Servings) (p. 50)

DINNER
Seared Salmon with
Lentil Salad (p. 62)

SNACK
Honey-Blueberry Oats (p. 77)

NOTES TO SELF
_____
_____
_____
_____
_____
_____
_____
_____
_____
_____
_____
_____
_____
_____
_____
_____
_____
_____

WATER

MOVEMENT/WORKOUT Y ☐ N ☐
ACTIVITY: _____
_____

DURATION: _____
_____

INTENSITY: _____
_____

SLEEP
Bedtime Last Night: _____ : _____
Wake Time This Morning: _____ : _____
_____
_____
_____

MOOD
☺ ☺ ☹
_____
_____
_____
_____

CONNECTION
_____
_____
_____
_____
_____

DAY 2

BREAKFAST

Vegan Coconut Chia Pudding
(1 cup) (p. 44)

LUNCH

Greek Salad + 4 oz Grilled
Chicken Breast (p. 52)

DINNER

Pork Tenderloin with
Quinoa Pilaf (p. 64)

SNACK

Best-Ever Spinach Artichoke
Dip + 10 Pita Chips (p. 77)

NOTES TO SELF

_____

_____

_____

_____

_____

_____

_____

_____

_____

_____

_____

_____

_____

_____

WATER

MOVEMENT/WORKOUT Y ☐ N ☐
ACTIVITY: _____

_____

DURATION: _____

_____

INTENSITY: _____

_____

SLEEP

Bedtime Last Night: _____ : _____
Wake Time This Morning: _____ : _____

_____

_____

MOOD

☺ ☹ ☹

_____

_____

_____

CONNECTION

_____

_____

_____

_____

DAY 3

BREAKFAST
No-Bake Fruit and Nut Bars
(2 Bars) (p. 46)

LUNCH
Citrusy Shrimp-Stuffed
Avocados (p. 54)

DINNER
Pan-Fried Chicken with
Lemony Roasted Broccoli
+ 1 cup Cooked Quinoa Pilaf
(Premade or Leftover)
(p. 66)

SNACK
1 5.3-oz Container Low-Sugar
Flavored Greek Yogurt

NOTES TO SELF
_____
_____
_____
_____
_____
_____
_____
_____
_____
_____
_____
_____
_____
_____
_____

WATER

MOVEMENT/WORKOUT Y ☐ N ☐
ACTIVITY: _____
_____
_____
DURATION: _____
_____
INTENSITY: _____
_____

SLEEP
Bedtime Last Night: _____ : _____
Wake Time This Morning: _____ : _____
_____
_____
_____

MOOD
☺   😐   ☹

_____
_____
_____

CONNECTION
_____
_____
_____
_____

DAY 4

BREAKFAST
Vegan Coconut Chia Pudding
(1 cup) (p. 44)

LUNCH
Whole-Grain Pita with
Leftover Pan-Fried Chicken
& Spinach Artichoke Dip
(p. 66, 77)

DINNER
Roasted Squash and Couscous
Salad (p. 68)

SNACK
1 cup Fresh-Cut
Vegetable Crudité

NOTES TO SELF
_____
_____
_____
_____
_____
_____
_____
_____
_____
_____
_____
_____
_____
_____
_____
_____
_____
_____

WATER

MOVEMENT/WORKOUT Y ☐ N ☐
ACTIVITY: _____
_____
DURATION: _____
_____
INTENSITY: _____
_____

SLEEP
Bedtime Last Night: _____ : _____
Wake Time This Morning: _____ : _____
_____
_____
_____

MOOD
☺ 😐 🙁

_____
_____
_____

CONNECTION
_____
_____
_____
_____

DAY 5

BREAKFAST
Blueberry-Banana-Nut
Smoothie (p. 46)

LUNCH
White Bean and Tuna Salad
with Basil Vinaigrette
+ 10 Pita Chips (p. 56)

DINNER
Mini Meatballs with Garlicky
Tomatoes (p. 70)

SNACKS
No-Bake Fruit and Nut Bar
(p. 46)
2 Squares 70% Dark Chocolate

NOTES TO SELF

WATER

MOVEMENT/WORKOUT Y ☐ N ☐
ACTIVITY: _____

DURATION: _____

INTENSITY: _____

SLEEP
Bedtime Last Night: _____ : _____
Wake Time This Morning: _____ : _____

MOOD
☺ ☺ ☹

CONNECTION

DAY 6

BREAKFAST
Shakshuka + 2 Slices Sprouted
Grain Bread (p. 48)

LUNCH
Grilled Halloumi Salad (p. 58)

DINNER
Fennel Roasted Chicken and
Peppers (p. 72) + 1 Large
Sweet Potato with 1 Tbsp
Butter, Sea Salt and Pepper

SNACK
½ cup Crunchy
Chickpea Snacks

NOTES TO SELF

WATER

MOVEMENT/WORKOUT Y ☐ N ☐
ACTIVITY: _____

DURATION: _____

INTENSITY: _____

SLEEP
Bedtime Last Night: _____ : _____
Wake Time This Morning: _____ : _____

MOOD
☺ ☺ ☹

CONNECTION

DAY 7

BREAKFAST

Orange and Pear Bran
Muffin (p. 45) + 1 5.3-oz
Container Low-Sugar
Flavored Greek Yogurt

LUNCH

Butternut Squash White
Bean Soup (p. 60)

DINNER

Shrimp and Zoodles Sheet
Pan Dinner (2 Servings)
(p. 74)

SNACK

1 cup Lightly Salted
Pistachios with Shells

NOTES TO SELF

_____
_____
_____
_____
_____
_____
_____
_____
_____
_____
_____
_____

WATER

MOVEMENT/WORKOUT Y ☐ N ☐

ACTIVITY: _____
_____
_____

DURATION: _____
_____

INTENSITY: _____
_____
_____

SLEEP

Bedtime Last Night: _____ : _____
Wake Time This Morning: _____ : _____
_____
_____
_____

MOOD

☺ ☺ ☹

_____
_____
_____
_____

CONNECTION

_____
_____
_____
_____

RECIPES

Spinach and Pepper Mini Frittatas

ACTIVE: 25 MIN. ✂ TOTAL: 45 MIN. ✂ SERVES 6

1   Tbsp olive oil
1   large red pepper, cut into
    ¼-in. pieces
    Kosher salt and pepper
2   scallions, chopped
3   large eggs plus 3 large
    egg whites
½   cup 1% milk
1   5-oz pkg. baby spinach,
    chopped
3   Tbsp fresh goat
    cheese, crumbled

1. Heat oven to 350°F. Spray 12-cup muffin pan with nonstick cooking spray.

2. Heat oil in large skillet on medium. Add red pepper and ⅛ tsp each salt and pepper and cook, covered, stirring occasionally, until tender, 6 to 8 min. Remove from heat and stir in scallions.

3. In large bowl, beat together eggs, egg whites, milk and ⅛ tsp each salt and pepper. Stir in spinach and red pepper mixture.

4. Divide batter among muffin pan cups (about ¼ cup each), top with goat cheese and bake until just set in center, 20 to 25 min. (Even when set, tops of frittatas may look wet from the spinach.)

5. Cool on wire rack 5 min., then remove from pan. Serve warm. Can be refrigerated up to 4 days; microwave on High 30 sec. to reheat.

Per serving About 150 cal, 8.5 g fat (2.5 g sat), 11 g pro, 285 mg sodium, 7 g carb, 2 fiber

**MAKE
IT AHEAD**
*Store frittatas in an
airtight container for up
to 4 days. Eat cold, at
room temperature or
microwave on medium
until heated
through.*

**MAKE
IT AHEAD**
*Transfer chia pudding
into 8-oz canning jars or
airtight containers and
refrigerate for up to 4 days.
You can pull them out as
needed and pile on your
favorite toppings.*

Vegan Coconut Chia Pudding

ACTIVE: 5 MIN ✼ TOTAL: 2 HR. 5 MIN. ✼ MAKES 3 CUPS

½   cup black chia seeds
3   Tbsp agave syrup
2   tsp pure vanilla extract
⅛   tsp Kosher salt
1   14-oz can coconut
    milk, shaken
1   cup almond or other
    nondairy milk
    Fresh berries, for serving
    Pepitas, for serving

1. In large bowl, combine chia seeds, syrup, vanilla and ⅛ tsp salt, making sure there are no clumps. Whisk in coconut and almond milks.

2. Transfer to a jar, cover and refrigerate at least 2 hr. Serve topped with fresh berries and pepitas.

Per ½-cup serving about 253 cal, 19.5 g fat (12.5 g sat), 4 g pro, 79 mg sodium, 17 g carb, 7 g fiber

Orange and Pear Bran Muffins

ACTIVE: 25 MIN. ✳ TOTAL: 50 MIN. ✳ MAKES 10

½ cup plus 2 tsp sugar
2 tsp orange zest
1 cup wheat bran
1 cup whole-wheat flour
1 tsp baking powder
½ tsp baking soda
½ tsp ground cinnamon
1 pinch kosher salt
¼ cup unsweetened applesauce
½ cup buttermilk
¼ cup olive oil
1 large egg
1 medium red pear

1. Heat oven to 350°F and line a 12-cup muffin pan with 10 paper liners. In small bowl, combine 2 tsp sugar with 2 tsp orange zest. Set aside.

2. In medium bowl, combine remaining ½ cup sugar, wheat bran, flour, baking powder, soda, cinnamon and salt.

3. In large bowl, combine applesauce, buttermilk, oil and egg. Add flour mixture to the bowl and mix to combine. Cut half pear into ¼-in. pieces and fold into the batter. Divide batter among lined muffin cups. Thinly slice remaining pear and arrange on top of batter. Sprinkle with orange sugar and bake until a wooden pick inserted in the middle comes out clean, 25 to 30 min. Let muffins cool in the pan for 5 min., then transfer to wire rack.

About 155 cal, 6.5 g fat (1 g sat), 4 g pro, 160 mg sodium, 24 g carb, 4 g fiber

No-Bake Fruit and Nut Bars

ACTIVE: 15 MIN. ✖ **TOTAL: 45 MIN.** ✖ **SERVES 12**

1	cup pitted dates (about 12)
¼	cup peanut or almond butter
¼	cup honey
1	tsp pure vanilla extract
1	cup roasted unsalted almonds, roughly chopped
½	cup rolled oats
¾	cup dried fruit (cranberries, golden raisins, sliced apricots)
¾	cup pepitas

1. Line an 8-in. square pan with nonstick foil, leaving an overhang on all sides.

2. In food processor, chop dates (they will form a ball); transfer to bowl.

3. In small saucepan over medium heat, melt peanut butter, honey and vanilla, stirring occasionally, until combined, about 1 min. Add to bowl and mix to combine.

4. Fold in almonds, oats, dried fruit and pepitas. Press mixture into prepared pan and freeze until sliceable, about 30 min. Cut into 12 bars.

About 214 cal, 10.5 g fat (1.5 g sat), 5 g pro, 38 mg sodium, 28 g carb, 4 g fiber

Blueberry-Banana-Nut Smoothie

ACTIVE: 5 MIN. ✖ **TOTAL: 5 MIN.** ✖ **SERVES 1**

1	cup unsweetened almond milk
1	frozen banana
½	cup frozen blueberries
2	Tbsp almond butter

In a blender, add ingredients in the order they are listed. Puree ingredients until smooth.

About 380 cal, 22 g fat (2 g sat), 10 g pro, 184 mg sodium, 45 g total carb, 9 g fiber

Shakshuka

ACTIVE: 15 MIN. ✂ TOTAL: 35 MIN. ✂ SERVES 4

2	Tbsp olive oil
1	yellow onion, finely chopped
1	clove garlic, finely chopped
1	tsp ground cumin
	Kosher salt and pepper
1	lb tomatoes, halved if large
8	large eggs
¼	cup baby spinach, finely chopped

1. Heat oven to 400°F. Heat oil in large oven-safe skillet on medium. Add onion and sauté until golden brown and tender, 8 min. Stir in garlic, cumin and ½ tsp each salt and pepper and cook 1 min. Stir in tomatoes, transfer to oven and roast 10 min.

2. Remove pan from oven, stir, then make 8 small wells in vegetable mixture and carefully crack 1 egg into each. Bake eggs to desired doneness, 7 to 8 min. for slightly runny yolks. Sprinkle with spinach.

About 235 cal, 16.5 g fat (4 g sat), 14 g pro, 390 mg sodium, 8 g carb, 2 g fiber

MAKE IT AHEAD
If you are only cooking for 1 or 2 people, prepare the entire tomato mixture, but only cook as many eggs as you plan on eating. The tomato mixture can be refrigerated in an airtight container for up to 5 days. When ready for seasoned tomatoes and eggs again, just warm some of the tomato mixture in a small oven-safe skillet. Add 2 eggs and bake per recipe directions.

Roasted Tomato Soup with Parmesan Crostini

ACTIVE: 10 MIN. ⁘ TOTAL: 1 HR. 20 MIN. ⁘ SERVES 4

- $2\frac{3}{4}$ lbs tomatoes
- 8 cloves garlic, smashed
- 1 red onion, thickly sliced
- 2 Tbsp olive oil
- Kosher salt and pepper
- 1 baguette, sliced (about $4\frac{1}{2}$-in.-thick)
- 3 Tbsp finely grated Parmesan

1. Heat oven to 325°F. On a rimmed baking sheet, toss tomatoes, garlic and onion with oil and ½ tsp each salt and pepper. Roast until tomatoes are tender and juicy and onion is tender, 60 to 70 min. Transfer all vegetables to pot along with 4 cups water and bring to a boil. Then, using an immersion blender (or standard blender, in batches), puree until smooth.

2. Heat oven to broil. Arrange baguette slices on baking sheet, top with Parmesan and broil until melted; serve with soup.

About 185 cal, 8.5 g fat (1.5 g sat), 6 g pro, 395 mg sodium, 24 g carb, 5 g fiber

Greek Salad

ACTIVE: 20 MIN. ✂ TOTAL: 20 MIN. ✂ SERVES 4 ✂

3 Tbsp red wine vinegar

2 Tbsp olive oil

2 tsp confectioners' sugar
   Kosher salt and pepper

2 Tbsp capers, drained and roughly chopped

1 tsp chopped fresh oregano

1 lb mixed cherry, grape and Campari tomatoes (halved or cut into wedges)

2 Persian cucumbers, cut into ¼-in.-thick rounds

½ very small red onion, thinly sliced

⅓ cup pitted Kalamata olives, halved
   Feta cheese, cut into small cubes, for serving

1. In small bowl, whisk together vinegar, oil, sugar and ¼ tsp each salt and pepper. Stir in capers and oregano.

2. Arrange tomatoes and cucumbers on a platter and scatter onion and olives on top. Spoon dressing over salad and top with feta if desired.

About 125 cal, 9.5 g fat (1.5 g sat), 2 g pro, 395 mg sodium, 9 g carb, 2 g fiber

MAKE IT AHEAD
Prepare the vinaigrette, but don't toss all of the ingredients at once. Refrigerate salad ingredients and the prepared vinaigrette separately, then combine just before serving.

Citrusy Shrimp-Stuffed Avocados

ACTIVE: 15 MIN. ✻ TOTAL: 35 MIN. ✻ SERVES 2

½ small shallot,
  finely chopped
2 Tbsp mayonnaise
1½ Tbsp sour cream
1½ Tbsp lime juice
1 Tbsp orange juice
½ tsp salt
½ lb cooked shelled
  shrimp, chopped
½ cup grape tomatoes,
  halved
½ serrano chile, thinly sliced
1 ripe avocado, halved,
  pit removed
  Cilantro and sweet potato
  chips, for serving

1. In small bowl, whisk shallot, mayonnaise, sour cream, lime juice, orange juice and ½ tsp salt.

2. In large bowl, toss shrimp, tomatoes, chile and half of dressing. Refrigerate 20 min.

3. To serve, spoon into avocado halves and drizzle with remaining dressing. Garnish with cilantro and serve.

About 420 cal, 29 g fat (5 g sat), 31 g pro,
395 mg sodium, 13 g carb, 7 g fiber

White Bean and Tuna Salad with Basil Vinaigrette

ACTIVE: 20 MIN. ✂ TOTAL: 25 MIN. ✂ SERVES 4

Kosher salt and pepper

12 oz green beans, trimmed and halved

1 small shallot, finely chopped

1 cup lightly packed basil leaves

3 Tbsp olive oil

1 Tbsp red wine vinegar

4 cups torn lettuce

1 15-oz can small white beans, rinsed

2 5-oz cans solid white tuna in water, drained

4 soft-boiled eggs, halved

1. Bring large pot of water to a boil. Add 1 Tbsp salt, then green beans, and cook until just tender, 3 to 4 min. Drain and rinse under cold water to cool.

2. Meanwhile, in a blender, puree shallot, basil, oil, vinegar and ½ tsp each salt and pepper until smooth.

3. Transfer half of vinaigrette to large bowl and toss with green beans. Fold in lettuce, white beans and tuna and serve with remaining dressing and eggs.

About 340 cal, 16.5 g fat (3 g sat), 31 g pro, 770 mg sodium, 24 g carb, 8 g fiber

**MAKE
IT AHEAD**

*Refrigerate vinaigrette,
blanched green beans and
remaining salad ingredients
separately for up to 2 days. Make
jammy eggs and refrigerate in their
shells for up to 3 days. If you prefer them
warm, you can reheat them by bringing
½ in. water to a boil and cooking,
covered, for 3½ min. Then peel
and serve. Combine salad
ingredients just before
serving.*

Grilled Halloumi Salad

ACTIVE: 20 MIN. ✂ TOTAL: 45 MIN. ✂ SERVES 4

1 cup Israeli (pearl) cous-cous or quick-cooking farro

8 oz asparagus, trimmed

4 oz snap peas, strings removed

3 tsp olive oil, divided
 Kosher salt and pepper

4½ oz Halloumi cheese, thinly sliced (about ⅛-in. thick)

1 tsp grated lemon zest plus 2 Tbsp lemon juice

1 scallion, thinly sliced

¼ cup fresh dill, chopped

¼ cup fresh flat-leaf parsley, chopped

1. Cook couscous per pkg. directions; drain, let cool and then transfer to large bowl. Heat grill to medium-high.

2. In second bowl, toss asparagus and snap peas with 1 tsp oil and ⅛ tsp each salt and pepper. Grill, turning or rolling once, until lightly charred and tender, 2 to 4 min.; transfer to cutting board.

3. Grill Halloumi until lightly charred, about 20 sec. per side; transfer to plate.

4. Cut asparagus into 1-in. pieces and snap peas into halves or thirds and toss with couscous, lemon zest and juice, remaining 2 tsp oil and ¼ tsp each salt and pepper. Fold in scallion, dill and parsley.

5. Tear Halloumi into bite-size pieces and fold into couscous.

About 330 cal, 12.5 g fat (6.5 g sat), 14 g pro, 525 mg sodium, 41 g carb, 4 g fiber

**MAKE
IT AHEAD**
*Refrigerate couscous,
grilled veggies and Halloumi
separately for up to 2 days.
When ready to serve, warm
couscous. Toss veggies with
couscous, lemon zest and juice,
then fold in scallions and
herbs and tear Halloumi
as directed.*

Butternut Squash White Bean Soup

ACTIVE: 20 MIN. ✂ TOTAL: 45 MIN. ✂ SERVES 4

1	large butternut squash
2	Tbsp olive oil
1	onion, chopped
2	cloves garlic, finely chopped
1	1-in. piece fresh ginger, finely chopped
6	cups low-sodium chicken broth
6	sprigs fresh thyme
1	15-oz can white beans, rinsed
1	15-oz can chickpeas, rinsed
½	cup couscous
¼	cup roasted pistachios, finely chopped
¼	cup dried apricots, finely chopped
¼	cup fresh cilantro, chopped
1	scallion, sliced

1. Cut neck off butternut squash (reserve base for another use). Peel and cut into ½-in. pieces. Heat 1 Tbsp olive oil in nonstick skillet on medium. Add squash and cook, covered, stirring occasionally, 8 min.

2. Meanwhile, heat remaining Tbsp oil in Dutch oven on medium. Add onion and cook, covered, stirring occasionally, 6 min. Stir in garlic and ginger and cook 1 min.

3. Add broth, thyme and butternut squash and bring to a boil. Using a fork, mash white beans and add to soup along with chickpeas.

4. Cook couscous per pkg. directions; fluff with fork and fold in pistachios, apricots, cilantro and scallion. Serve soup topped with couscous mixture.

About 560 cal, 15.5 g fat (2 g sat), 26 g pro, 385 mg sodium, 88 g carb, 19 g fiber

**MAKE
IT AHEAD**
*The soup and plain
couscous can be refriger-
ated separately for up to
3 days. Warm soup over
medium heat. Reheat couscous
in the microwave then fold in
pistachios, apricots and
cilantro and scallion
as directed.*

Seared Salmon with Lentil Salad

ACTIVE: 20 MIN. ✕ TOTAL: 20 MIN. ✕ SERVES 4

4	5-oz skinless salmon fillets
¼	tsp Kosher salt
¼	tsp pepper
2	Tbsp plus 2 tsp olive oil
2	lemons, halved
2	tsp Dijon mustard
1	tsp fresh thyme
½	small red onion, finely chopped
1	15-oz can lentils, rinsed
1	small seedless cucumber, cut into pieces
4	cups baby spinach
¼	cup fresh dill, very roughly chopped

1. Heat large skillet on medium. Season salmon fillets with ¼ tsp each kosher salt and pepper. Add 2 tsp oil to skillet, then salmon and lemon halves, cut-sides down, and cook until salmon is opaque throughout, 5 min. per side. Squeeze the charred lemon halves over salmon.

2. Meanwhile, in large bowl, squeeze 2 Tbsp lemon juice from remaining lemon halves. Add mustard, remaining 2 Tbsp oil and salt and pepper and whisk to combine; stir in thyme.

3. Toss with onion and lentils then fold in cucumber, spinach and dill. Serve with salmon.

About 350 cal, 13 g fat (2 g sat), 37 g pro, 490 mg sodium, 19 g carb, 9 g fiber

LOVE YOUR LEFTOVERS
Refrigerate any leftover salmon and lentil salad separately for up to 3 days. Flake the salmon and serve cold tossed with greens or stuffed into a piece of pita or sandwich wrap.

Pork Tenderloin with Quinoa Pilaf

ACTIVE: 25 MIN. ✖ TOTAL: 35 MIN. ✖ SERVES 4

2	Tbsp olive oil, divided
1	clove garlic, thinly sliced
1½	cups quinoa
4	cups baby spinach (about 5 oz)
2	small pork tenderloins (about ¾ lb each), cut into 4 equal pieces
	Kosher salt and pepper
2	Tbsp white wine vinegar
2	Tbsp orange marmalade
2	tsp Dijon mustard
½	cup pomegranate seeds

1. Heat 1 Tbsp oil in a medium saucepan on medium. Add garlic and cook, stirring occasionally, until toasted, about 2 min. Add quinoa and cook per pkg. directions. Fluff with a fork and fold in spinach.

2. While quinoa cooks, heat a skillet on medium. Add remaining Tbsp oil, season pork with ½ tsp each salt and pepper, and cook until browned on all sides and an instant-read thermometer registers 145°F, 12 to 14 min.

3. Meanwhile, in small bowl, whisk together vinegar, marmalade and mustard. Transfer pork to a cutting board and let rest 5 min. Discard any oil left in pan. Add mustard mixture to skillet and simmer until thickened, 2 to 3 min. Brush on pork.

4. Slice pork, serve over quinoa and sprinkle with pomegranate seeds.

   About 545 cal, 16 g fat (3 g sat), 45 g pro, 410 mg sodium, 54 g carb, 6 g fiber

LOVE YOUR LEFTOVERS

Only slice as much pork as you need for dinner tonight. Store the remaining pork and quinoa separately in airtight containers for up to 3 days. You can slice and serve the pork cold in sandwiches, cube and toss into salads or reheat, then slice and serve warm. Reheat quinoa in microwave, covered, in 30-second intervals until heated through.

Pan-Fried Chicken with Lemony Roasted Broccoli

ACTIVE: 25 MIN. ✂ TOTAL: 35 MIN. ✂ SERVES 4

1½ lbs broccoli, cut
into florets
2 cloves garlic, thinly sliced
3 Tbsp olive oil
Kosher salt and pepper
4 6-oz boneless, skinless
chicken breasts
1 cup all-purpose flour
1 lemon, cut into
½-in. pieces
2 Tbsp lemon juice

1. Heat oven to 425°F. On rimmed baking sheet, toss broccoli and garlic with 1 Tbsp oil and ¼ tsp each salt and pepper; roast 10 min.

2. Meanwhile, pound chicken breasts to even thickness, season with ¼ tsp each salt and pepper then coat in flour. Heat 1 Tbsp oil in large skillet on medium-high and cook chicken until golden brown, 3 to 5 min. per side. Nestle chicken amidst broccoli and roast until chicken is cooked through and broccoli is golden brown and tender, about 6 min.

3. Return skillet to medium heat; add remaining Tbsp oil, then lemon pieces, and cook, stirring, until beginning to brown, 3 min. Add lemon juice and ⅓ cup water and cook, stirring and scraping up any browned bits. Spoon over chicken and serve with broccoli.

About 365 cal, 15.5 g fat (2.5 g sat), 44 g pro, 375 mg sodium, 15 g carb, 5 g fiber

LOVE YOUR LEFTOVERS

This recipe can be easily halved, but consider making all 4 servings. You can refrigerate broccoli and chicken separately for up to 3 days. The broccoli is great on grain bowls, tossed in salads or chopped and used as a relish to jazz up your favorite sandwich. You can slice and use leftover chicken on the same sandwich or use chicken for another dish.

Roasted Squash and Couscous Salad

ACTIVE: 15 MIN. ✕ **TOTAL: 35 MIN.** ✕ **SERVES 4**

1   medium butternut squash
(about 2¼ lbs), peeled
and cut into ½-in. pieces

2½ Tbsp olive oil, divided
      Kosher salt and pepper

1½ cups Israeli (pearl)
      couscous

2   Tbsp balsamic vinegar

2   tsp honey

½   small red onion,
      thinly sliced

4   cups baby arugula

½   cup blanched almonds,
      toasted and
      roughly chopped

2   oz pecorino cheese,
      shaved with a peeler

1. Heat oven to 450°F. On a rimmed baking sheet, toss squash with 1 Tbsp oil and ½ tsp each salt and pepper. Roast until golden brown and tender, 20 to 25 min.

2. Meanwhile, cook couscous per pkg. directions. Drain and refrigerate until ready to use.

3. In a large bowl, whisk together balsamic vinegar, honey and remaining 1½ Tbsp oil. Toss in onion and let sit 5 min.

4. Toss couscous with onion mixture, then fold in squash, arugula, almonds and pecorino.

About 620 cal, 21.5 g fat (4.5 g sat), 21 g pro, 435 mg sodium, 89 g carb, 10 g fiber

**MAKE
IT AHEAD**
Roasted squash, cooked
couscous and dressing can be
refrigerated separately for up to
3 days. When ready to serve,
combine components per recipe
instructions, and toss together
only what you need. The rest
can be eaten together or
divided and added to
other meals.

Mini Meatballs with Garlicky Tomatoes

ACTIVE: 45 MIN. ✂ TOTAL 45 MIN. ✂ SERVES 4

1	large egg
¼	cup panko
4	cloves garlic, 2 finely chopped, 2 crushed with press
2	cups packed baby spinach, 1 cup finely chopped, 1 cup thinly sliced
¼	cup finely grated Parmesan
½	tsp dried oregano
	Kosher salt and pepper
1	lb ground beef
1	lb Campari tomatoes
1	Tbsp olive oil

1. Heat oven to 450°F. In bowl, whisk together egg and 2 Tbsp water. Add panko and let sit until liquid is absorbed.

2. Add chopped garlic, chopped spinach, Parmesan, oregano and ½ tsp each salt and pepper and mix to combine. Add beef and mix until combined.

3. Form into tiny balls (about 1 level tsp each, about 92 balls) and place on prepared baking sheet. Broil until browned, 6 to 8 min.

4. Halve tomatoes and arrange, cut sides up, on second baking sheet. Drizzle with oil and sprinkle tops with pressed garlic and pinch each salt and pepper. Broil until garlic is fragrant, 3 to 4 min. Serve meatballs with tomatoes and sliced spinach.

About 310 cal, 16.5 g fat (5.5 g sat), 29 g pro, 505 mg sodium, 11 g carb, 2 g fiber

MAKE IT AHEAD
Refrigerate cooked meatballs for up to 4 days. Warm in the microwave or oven along with the tomatoes.

Fennel Roasted Chicken and Peppers

ACTIVE: 15 MIN. ✂ **TOTAL: 35 MIN.** ✂ **SERVES 4**

1	Tbsp fennel seeds
1	Tbsp finely grated orange zest
3	bell peppers (red, yellow and orange), cut into 1-in. chunks
6	cloves garlic, thinly sliced
2	Tbsp olive oil
	Kosher salt and pepper
4	small chicken legs (about 2 lbs)
4	cups baby spinach
2	oz feta cheese, crumbled

1. Heat oven to 425°F. In small skillet, toast fennel seeds and orange zest until lightly browned and fragrant, 3 to 4 min. Transfer to spice grinder or blender and pulse to blend and grind. Set aside.

2. On large rimmed baking sheet, toss bell peppers and garlic with 1 Tbsp oil and ½ tsp each salt and pepper. Rub chicken legs with remaining Tbsp oil, then with fennel-orange mixture. Nestle among vegetables on baking sheet and roast until chicken is golden brown and cooked through and peppers are tender, 25 to 30 min.

3. Transfer chicken to plates, scatter spinach over peppers remaining on sheet and toss until just beginning to wilt (pop back in oven, if necessary). Sprinkle with feta and serve with chicken.

About 350 cal, 25 g fat (7 g sat), 25 g pro, 350 mg sodium, 11 g carb, 3 g fiber

Shrimp and Zoodles Sheet Pan Dinner

ACTIVE: 20 MIN. ✂ TOTAL: 25 MIN. ✂ SERVES 4

1½ lbs spiralized zucchini
2   Tbsp olive oil
      Kosher salt and pepper
20   large peeled and
      deveined shrimp
4   scallions, thinly sliced
4   cloves garlic, thinly sliced
1   small red chile,
      thinly sliced
2   Tbsp dry white wine
1   Tbsp fresh lemon juice
4   oz feta, crumbled

1. Heat oven to 475°F. On a large rimmed baking sheet, toss zucchini with 1 Tbsp oil and ¼ tsp each salt and pepper; arrange in an even layer and roast 6 min.

2. Meanwhile, in a bowl, toss shrimp, scallions, garlic and chile with wine, lemon juice and ¼ tsp each salt and pepper.

3. Scatter shrimp over zucchini, drizzle with remaining Tbsp oil and sprinkle with feta. Roast until shrimp are opaque throughout, 5 to 7 min.

About 200 cal, 13.5 g fat (5.5 g sat), 11 g pro, 715 mg sodium, 10 g carb, 2 g fiber

Honey-Blueberry Oats

ACTIVE: 10 MIN ✖ TOTAL: 10 MIN ✖ SERVES 1

½   cup dry old-
    fashioned oats
1   cup 1% milk
½   cup blueberries
    Cinnamon
1   Tbsp honey

Cook oats per pkg. directions, using milk. Top with blueberries, cinnamon and honey.

About 364 cal, 5 g fat (0 g sat fat), 14 g pro, 110 mg sodium, 69 g carb, 7 g fiber

Best-Ever Spinach Artichoke Dip

ACTIVE: 5 MIN. ✖ TOTAL: 5 MIN. ✖ MAKES 1¾ CUPS

1   14-oz can artichoke
    hearts, rinsed, squeezed
    of excess moisture and
    patted dry
1   cup packed baby spinach
½   cup canned cannellini
    beans, rinsed
1   scallion, chopped
    Finely grated zest of 1
    lemon (about 1 Tbsp) plus
    2 Tbsp juice
1   oz finely grated Parmesan
    Black pepper

In blender, puree artichoke hearts, spinach, beans, scallion, lemon zest and juice, Parmesan and ½ tsp pepper until finely chopped.

Per ¼ cup about 55 cal, 1 g fat (0.5 g sat), 3.5 g pro, 195 mg sodium, 7 g carb, 2 g fiber

**MAKE
IT AHEAD**
*Refrigerate dip
in an airtight
container for up
to 3 days.*

WEEK 2 At-a-Glance

DAY 8

BREAKFAST
⏱ Classic Omelet and Greens

LUNCH
Broccoli Steaks with
Spicy Tomato Jam
+ ½ cup Chickpeas

DINNER
⏱ Chicken Bolognese

SNACK
1 5.3-oz Container Low-Sugar
Flavored Greek Yogurt

DAY 9

BREAKFAST
Blueberry-Banana-Nut
Smoothie

LUNCH
⏱ White Bean and Kale Toasts

DINNER
Cod in Parchment with
Orange Leek Couscous

SNACK
½ cup Crunchy
Chickpea Snacks

DAY 10

BREAKFAST
⏱ Spinach and Pepper Mini
Frittatas + 1 Slice Sprouted
Grain Bread

LUNCH
⏱ Chickpea Pasta Salad

DINNER
⏱ Beef Kofta with Kale and
Chickpea Salad

SNACK
⏱ Orange and Pear
Bran Muffin

DAY 11

BREAKFAST
Spring Radish and Avocado
Toast

LUNCH
⏱ Chicken Roulades with
Marinated Tomatoes + 1 cup
Cooked Quinoa Pilaf Blend

DINNER
⏱ Summer Minestrone
+ 10 Pita Chips

SNACK
Hummus-Stuffed Peppers

DAY 12

BREAKFAST
⏱ Grain Bowl with Sautéed
Spinach

LUNCH
⏱ Butternut Squash White
Bean Soup

DINNER
Pork with Roasted Asparagus
and Apricot Relish

SNACK
⏱ No-Bake Fruit and Nut Bar

DAY 13

BREAKFAST
Strawberry-Almond Oats

LUNCH
⏱ Summer Minestrone
+ 1 Whole-Grain Pita

DINNER
Roasted Salmon with Charred
Lemon Vinaigrette

SNACK
½ cup Lightly Salted
Mixed Nuts

DAY 14

BREAKFAST
⏱ Classic Omelet and Greens

LUNCH
⏱ Caponata Flatbread

DINNER
Skillet Pesto Chicken
and Beans

SNACK
½ cup Crunchy
Chickpea Snacks

Check for leftover ingredients from Week 1 before purchasing new ingredients from the shopping list.

PRODUCE

Veggies

- 2 heads garlic
- 2 small yellow onions
- 2 large yellow onions
- 3¼ red onions
- 1 small carrot
- 8 oz red potatoes
- 1 large butternut squash
- 1 1-in. piece fresh ginger
- 3 leeks (2 thin)
- 2 bulbs fennel
- 3 red peppers
- 1 small zucchini
- 1 yellow squash
- 1 small eggplant (about 12 oz)
- 2 broccoli crowns
- 1 lb asparagus
- 8 oz green beans
- 4 scallions
- 2 small radishes
- 5 pints plus 1 cup cherry or grape tomatoes
- 1 medium tomato
- 2 plum tomatoes
- 1 avocado

Greens & Lettuce

- 3 5-oz pkgs. baby spinach
- 2 5-oz pkgs. baby kale
- 1 bunch spinach
- 1 5-oz pkg. baby arugula

Herbs

- 1 cup flat-leaf parsley
- 1 cup fresh basil
- ¼ cup chopped chives
- ¼ cup fresh cilantro
- ¼ cup mint
- 6 sprigs fresh thyme
- 1 Tbsp tarragon

Fruit

- 3 lemons
- 1 orange
- ½ cup strawberries
- 1 banana

MEAT & SEAFOOD

- 4 boneless, skinless chicken breasts
- 8 small chicken thighs (about 2 lbs)
- 1 lb ground chicken
- 1 lb ground beef
- 1¼ lbs pork tenderloin
- 1¼ lbs skin-on salmon fillet

REFRIGERATED & DAIRY

- 2 Tbsp unsalted butter
- 18 large eggs
- 1½ cups 1% milk
- 1 cup unsweetened almond milk
- 1 5.3-oz container low-sugar flavored Greek yogurt
- ¼ cup crumbled feta
- 3 Tbsp fresh goat cheese, crumbled
- 8 oz Parmesan (about 2 cups grated)
- 1 cup part-skim ricotta
- 1 lb pizza dough
- ¼ cup hummus
- 2 Tbsp prepared pesto

FROZEN

- ½ cup frozen blueberries
- ½ cup frozen peas

BREAD & BAKERY

- 1 small baguette
- 1 slice sprouted grain bread
- 1 thin slice whole-grain bread
- 1 whole-grain pita

PANTRY

Oils, Vinegars, Condiments & Spices

- ½ cup white wine vinegar
- 6 Tbsp red wine vinegar
- 1 tsp Dijon mustard
- 1 tsp stone-ground mustard

Grains

- ½ cup rotini
- 12 oz rigatoni
- 1½ cups couscous
- ¼ cup quinoa pilaf blend
- ¼ to ¾ cup grain (such as farro, brown rice or quinoa)
- 1 cup old-fashioned rolled oats

Beans & Veggies

- 3 15-oz cans chickpeas
- 2 15-oz cans white beans
- 1 15-oz can butter beans
- 2 Tbsp Kalamata olives
- 1 Tbsp capers

Broth & Wine

- 6½ cups low-sodium chicken broth
- 4 cups low-sodium vegetable broth
- ½ cup dry white wine

Baking

- ⅓ cup honey

Nuts, Seeds & Fruits

- 1 cup roasted unsalted almonds
- ½ cup lightly salted mixed nuts
- ¼ cup roasted pistachios
- 2 Tbsp sliced almonds
- ¾ cup pepitas
- ¼ cup peanut or almond butter
- 1 cup (about 12) pitted dates
- ¾ cup dried fruit (cranberries, golden raisins, sliced apricots)
- ½ cup dried apricots

Chips

- 1 cup crunchy chickpea snacks

DAY 8

BREAKFAST

Classic Omelet and Greens
(p. 88)

LUNCH

Broccoli Steaks with Spicy
Tomato Jam (p. 94)
+ ½ cup Chickpeas

DINNER

Chicken Bolognese (p. 104)

SNACK

1 5.3-oz Container Low-Sugar
Flavored Greek Yogurt

NOTES TO SELF

WATER

MOVEMENT/WORKOUT Y ☐ N ☐
ACTIVITY: _____

DURATION: _____

INTENSITY: _____

SLEEP
Bedtime Last Night: _____ : _____
Wake Time This Morning: _____ : _____

MOOD

CONNECTION

DAY 9

BREAKFAST
Blueberry-Banana-Nut
Smoothie (p. 46)

LUNCH
White Bean and Kale Toasts
(2 Servings) (p. 96)

DINNER
Cod in Parchment with
Orange Leek Couscous
(p. 106)

SNACK
½ cup Crunchy
Chickpea Snacks

NOTES TO SELF
_____
_____
_____
_____
_____
_____
_____
_____
_____
_____
_____
_____
_____
_____
_____
_____
_____
_____

WATER

MOVEMENT/WORKOUT Y ☐ N ☐
ACTIVITY: _____
_____
DURATION: _____
_____
INTENSITY: _____
_____

SLEEP
Bedtime Last Night: _____ : _____
Wake Time This Morning: _____ : _____
_____
_____
_____

MOOD
☺ 😐 ☹

CONNECTION
_____
_____
_____

DAY 10

BREAKFAST
Spinach and Pepper Mini Frittatas (2 Servings) (p. 42) + 1 Slice Sprouted Grain Bread

LUNCH
Chickpea Pasta Salad (p. 98)

DINNER
Beef Kofta with Kale and Chickpea Salad (p. 108)

SNACK
Orange and Pear Bran Muffin (p. 45)

NOTES TO SELF

WATER

MOVEMENT/WORKOUT Y ☐ N ☐
ACTIVITY: _____

DURATION: _____

INTENSITY: _____

SLEEP
Bedtime Last Night: _____ : _____
Wake Time This Morning: _____ : _____

MOOD

CONNECTION

DAY 11

BREAKFAST
Spring Radish and Avocado
Toast (p. 90)

LUNCH
Chicken Roulades with
Marinated Tomatoes (p. 100)
+ 1 cup Cooked Quinoa
Pilaf Blend

DINNER
Summer Minestrone
(2 Servings) (p. 110)
+ 10 Pita Chips

SNACK
Hummus-Stuffed Peppers
(p. 116)

NOTES TO SELF

WATER

MOVEMENT/WORKOUT Y ☐ N ☐
ACTIVITY: _____

DURATION: _____

INTENSITY: _____

SLEEP
Bedtime Last Night: _____ : _____
Wake Time This Morning: _____ : _____

MOOD
☺ 😐 ☹

CONNECTION

DAY 12

BREAKFAST
Grain Bowl with Sautéed
Spinach (p. 92)

LUNCH
Butternut Squash White
Bean Soup (p. 60)

DINNER
Pork with Roasted Asparagus
and Apricot Relish (p. 112)

SNACK
No-Bake Fruit and Nut Bar
(p. 46)

NOTES TO SELF

WATER

MOVEMENT/WORKOUT Y ☐ N ☐
ACTIVITY: _____

DURATION: _____

INTENSITY: _____

SLEEP
Bedtime Last Night: _____ : _____
Wake Time This Morning: _____ : _____

MOOD
☺ ☺ ☹

CONNECTION

DAY 13

BREAKFAST
Strawberry-Almond Oats
(p. 92)

LUNCH
Summer Minestrone
(2 Servings) (p. 110)
+ 1 Whole-Grain Pita

DINNER
Roasted Salmon with Charred
Lemon Vinaigrette (p. 114)

SNACK
½ cup Lightly Salted
Mixed Nuts

NOTES TO SELF

WATER

MOVEMENT/WORKOUT Y ☐ N ☐
ACTIVITY: _____

DURATION: _____

INTENSITY: _____

SLEEP
Bedtime Last Night: _____ : _____
Wake Time This Morning: _____ : _____

MOOD
☺ ☺ ☹

CONNECTION

DAY 14

BREAKFAST
Classic Omelet and Greens
(p. 88)

LUNCH
Caponata Flatbread (p. 102)

DINNER
Skillet Pesto Chicken and
Beans (p. 116)

SNACK
½ cup Crunchy
Chickpea Snacks

NOTES TO SELF

_____
_____
_____
_____
_____
_____
_____
_____
_____
_____
_____
_____
_____
_____

WATER

MOVEMENT/WORKOUT Y ☐ N ☐
ACTIVITY: _____
_____
_____
DURATION: _____
_____
_____
INTENSITY: _____
_____
_____

SLEEP
_Bedtime Last Night: _____ : _____
_Wake Time This Morning: _____ : _____
_____
_____
_____

MOOD
☺ 😐 ☹
_____
_____
_____
_____

CONNECTION
_____
_____
_____
_____

WEEK 2
RECIPES

Classic Omelet and Greens

ACTIVE: 20 MIN. ✂ TOTAL: 20 MIN. ✂ SERVES 2

2	Tbsp olive oil, divided
1	small yellow onion, finely chopped
4	large eggs
	Kosher salt and pepper
1	Tbsp unsalted butter
½	oz Parmesan, finely grated (about ¼ cup)
1	Tbsp fresh lemon juice
4	cups baby spinach

1. Heat 1 Tbsp oil in medium nonstick skillet on medium. Add onion and sauté until tender, about 6 min. Transfer to a small bowl.

2. In large bowl, whisk together eggs, 1 Tbsp water and ½ tsp salt. Return skillet to medium and add butter. Add eggs and cook, stirring constantly with rubber spatula, until eggs are partially set. Turn heat to low and cover pan tightly, cooking until eggs are just set, 2 to 4 min. Top with Parmesan and cooked onion; fold in half.

3. In bowl, whisk together lemon juice, remaining Tbsp oil and pinch each salt and pepper. Toss with spinach and serve with omelet.

About 315 cal, 26 g fat (6 g sat), 17 g pro, 333 mg sodium, 7 g carb, 2 g fiber

MAKE IT AHEAD
If only serving 1, prepare enough salad for 1, but make the entire omelet. Refrigerate remaining omelet half in an airtight container for up to 2 days. Warm in a covered nonstick skillet on low or microwave in 20-second increments until heated through.

Spring Radish and Avocado Toast

ACTIVE: 10 MIN. ✂ **TOTAL: 10 MIN.** ✂ **SERVES 1**

1   thin slice whole-grain
      bread
½   avocado, smashed
      Lemon juice
1   hard-boiled egg,
      thinly sliced
2   small radishes, very
      thinly sliced
      Kosher salt and pepper
      Mint leaves

Toast bread. Top with avocado and drizzle with lemon juice. Top with egg and radishes. Sprinkle with pinch each salt and pepper, then fresh mint leaves.

About 290 cal, 21 g fat (4 g sat), 12 g pro, 300 mg sodium, 20 g carb, 9 g fiber

Grain Bowl with Sautéed Spinach

ACTIVE: 10 MIN. ✀ TOTAL: 10 MIN. ✀ SERVES 2

2 cups cooked grains (such as farro, brown rice, quinoa), warmed
1 Tbsp olive oil
1 clove garlic, finely chopped
1 bunch spinach, thick stems discarded, leaves roughly chopped (about 4 cups)
  Kosher salt and pepper
1 medium tomato, cut into 1-in. pieces
½ avocado, diced
2 large eggs
  parsley

1. Divide grains between 2 bowls. In a large nonstick skillet on medium, heat oil and garlic until garlic starts to turn golden brown, 1 min. Add spinach, salt and pepper and cook, tossing, until leaves begin to wilt, 1 to 2 min. Spoon on top of grains along with tomato and avocado.

2. Return skillet to medium heat and cook eggs to desired doneness, 2 to 3 min. for runny yolks. Serve on top of grain bowls.

About 415 cal, 11 g total fat (3 g sat fat), 17 g pro, 110 mg sodium, 66 g carb, 8 g fiber

Strawberry-Almond Oats

ACTIVE: 10 MIN. ✀ TOTAL: 10 MIN. ✀ SERVES 1

½ cup dry old-fashioned oats
1 cup 1% milk
½ cup strawberries
  Cinnamon
2 Tbsp sliced almonds
1 Tbsp honey

Cook oats per pkg. directions using milk. Serve topped with strawberries, cinnamon, sliced almonds and honey.

About 415 cal, 11 g total fat (3 g sat fat), 17 g pro, 110 mg sodium, 66 g carb, 8g fiber

MAKE
IT AHEAD
Prepare the grains and veggies and refrigerate separately in an airtight container for up to 2 days. Reheat, covered, in a small skillet on medium-low or microwave in 20-second increments. Top with tomato, avocado and egg before serving.

Broccoli Steaks with Spicy Tomato Jam

ACTIVE: 30 MIN. ✂ **TOTAL: 40 MIN.** ✂ **SERVES 4**

1 pint cherry tomatoes
¼ cup sugar
½ tsp chili powder
3½ oz roughly torn baguette
(generous 2 cups)
1½ oz finely grated Parmesan
2 Tbsp olive oil
2 broccoli crowns, each cut
in half
Kosher salt and pepper

1. Heat oven to 425°F. In small saucepan, simmer tomatoes, sugar, chili powder and ½ cup water until completely broken down and glossy, 20 to 25 min.

2. In food processor, pulse bread with Parmesan to form coarse crumbs. Spread on rimmed baking sheet and roast until golden brown, 4 to 5 min.

3. Heat large cast-iron skillet on medium high. Add oil, then broccoli crowns, cut sides down, and cook until golden brown, 5 to 6 min. Flip broccoli, season with ½ tsp each salt and pepper, transfer to oven and roast until just tender, about 16 min. Serve broccoli steak with tomato jam and crumbs.

About 265 cal, 10.5 g fat (2.5 g sat), 10 g pro, 595 mg sodium, 36 g carb, 4 g fiber

LOVE YOUR LEFTOVERS
Refrigerate broccoli and tomato jam separately in airtight containers for up to 3 days. Chop broccoli and use in salads, grain bowls or pasta. Use the tomato jam to upgrade your favorite morning toast or lunchtime sandwich.

White Bean and Kale Toasts

ACTIVE: 20 MIN. ✂ TOTAL: 20 MIN. ✂ SERVES 4

2	Tbsp olive oil
1	yellow onion, thinly sliced
2	cloves garlic, thinly sliced
1	15-oz can white beans, rinsed
3	cups baby kale
	Kosher salt and pepper
4	½-in.-thick slices baguette, toasted
2	hard-boiled eggs, finely grated
4	tsp finely grated Parmesan

1. Heat oil in large skillet on medium. Add onion and garlic and sauté until very tender, about 10 min.

2. Add beans and ⅓ cup water and heat through, about 3 min. Add kale, season with salt and pepper and toss until just beginning to wilt, 2 min. Top baguette slices with bean mixture, then eggs and Parmesan.

About 275 cal, 10.5 g fat (2 g sat), 13 g pro, 360 mg sodium, 32 g carb, 10 g fiber

MAKE IT AHEAD
Refrigerate the kale and white bean mixture for up to 3 days. Toast baguette, prepare eggs and reheat as needed and eat for breakfast, lunch or dinner. Or use the white beans and kale as a side for any protein.

Chickpea Pasta Salad

ACTIVE: 10 MIN. ✕ TOTAL: 10 MIN. ✕ SERVES 1

¼   very small red onion, finely chopped

2   Tbsp red wine vinegar

1½ Tbsp olive oil
Kosher salt and pepper

½   cup canned chickpeas, rinsed

1   cup grape tomatoes, halved

2   Tbsp Kalamata olives, halved

1   cup cooked rotini pasta

1½ cups baby arugula

2   Tbsp crumbled feta

1. In 1-quart jar, shake onion, vinegar, oil and pinch each salt and pepper.

2. Add chickpeas and gently shake to coat. Top with tomatoes, olives, pasta, arugula and feta.

3. When ready to serve, turn upside down and let sit 2 min. so dressing can run over rest of ingredients.

About 650 cal, 31.5 g fat (6.5 g sat), 19 g pro, 945 mg sodium, 72 g carb, 11 g fiber

**MAKE
IT AHEAD**
Can be prepared ahead and refrigerated up to 2 days. Let stand at room temp at least 10 min. before turning over to spread dressing.

Chicken Roulades with Marinated Tomatoes

ACTIVE: 35 MIN. ✂ TOTAL: 35 MIN. ✂ SERVES 4

4	boneless, skinless chicken breasts
2	cloves garlic, finely grated
2	Tbsp lemon zest plus 2 Tbsp lemon juice
½	cup finely grated Parmesan
32	baby spinach leaves
	Kosher salt and pepper
3	Tbsp olive oil, divided
2	pints grape or cherry tomatoes, sliced
¼	small red onion, thinly sliced
2	Tbsp red wine vinegar

1. Heat oven to 450°F. Pound chicken breasts into thin cutlets. In small bowl, combine garlic, lemon zest and Parmesan. Lay 8 spinach leaves on each chicken cutlet, then sprinkle garlic mixture on top. Roll chicken up and secure with a toothpick (place toothpick in parallel to seam to make turning roulades easier). Season chicken with ½ tsp each salt and pepper.

2. Heat 1 Tbsp oil in large ovenproof skillet on medium-high. Carefully add roulades, seam sides down, and cook, turning until browned on all sides, 6 to 7 min. Transfer to oven and bake until cooked through, 8 to 9 min. more. Drizzle lemon juice on roulades.

3. While chicken roasts, toss together tomatoes, onion, red wine vinegar, remaining 2 Tbsp oil and ½ tsp each salt and pepper. Serve with chicken.

About 310 cal, 16.5 g fat (4 g sat), 31 g pro,
735 mg sodium, 10 g carb, 3 g fiber

**MAKE
IT AHEAD**
*The chicken roulades can
be rolled up and refrigerated
raw for up to 2 days. Once
cooked, the roulades can be
refrigerated for up to 2 days. They
can be sliced cold and added to
sandwiches and salads. Prepare
the marinated tomatoes the
day you plan on serving
them.*

Caponata Flatbread

ACTIVE: 20 MIN. ✖ **TOTAL: 25 MIN.** ✖ **SERVES 4**

Flour, for surface

1   lb pizza dough, thawed
    if frozen

2   Tbsp red wine vinegar

1   tsp honey

2½ Tbsp olive oil, divided

2   plum tomatoes,
    halved lengthwise

1   small eggplant (about
    12 oz), halved lengthwise

1   red pepper, quartered
    Kosher salt and pepper

1   Tbsp capers, chopped

¼   cup flat-leaf parsley,
    roughly chopped

1   cup part-skim ricotta

1. Heat oven to 425°F and heat grill to medium-high. On lightly floured surface, shape pizza dough into large rectangle, transfer to a parchment-lined baking sheet, and bake 10 min. Remove from oven, then increase heat to 475°F.

2. Meanwhile, in large bowl, whisk together vinegar, honey and 1 Tbsp oil.

3. Brush tomatoes, eggplant and red pepper with 1 Tbsp oil and season with ¼ tsp each salt and pepper. Grill, turning occasionally, until just tender, 2 to 4 min. per side; transfer to a cutting board and cut into large pieces.

4. Add vegetables and capers to vinegar mixture and toss to combine; fold in parsley. Spread ricotta on crust, leaving a ½-in. border all the way around, then top with vegetables. Brush crust with remaining ½ Tbsp oil and bake until crust is deep golden brown, 4 to 6 min.

About 490 cal, 16 g fat (3 g sat), 18 g pro,
520 mg sodium, 66 g carb, 6 g fiber

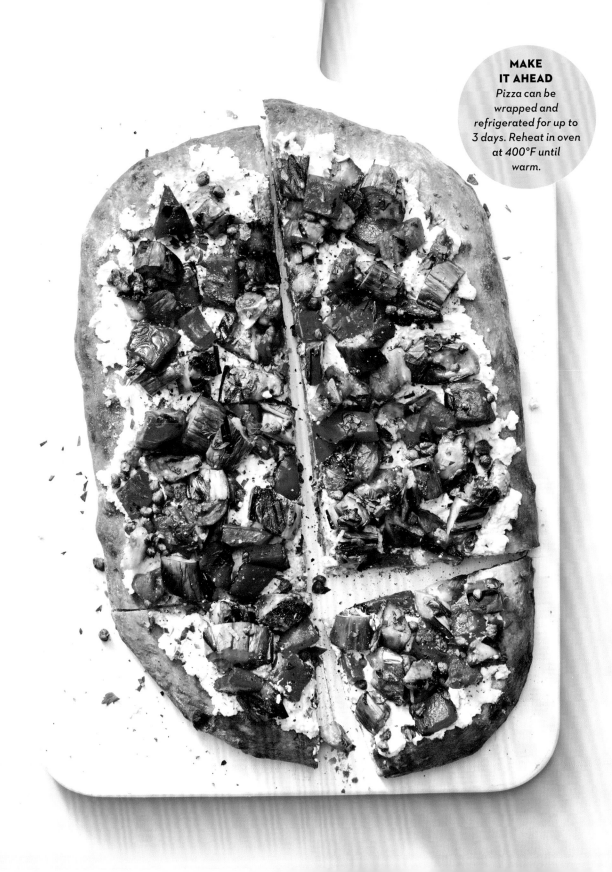

MAKE IT AHEAD
Pizza can be wrapped and refrigerated for up to 3 days. Reheat in oven at 400°F until warm.

Chicken Bolognese

ACTIVE: 15 MIN. ✕ TOTAL: 20 MIN. ✕ SERVES 4

12	oz mezze rigatoni
1	Tbsp olive oil
2	cloves garlic, pressed
1	lb ground chicken
½	tsp red pepper flakes
	Kosher salt and pepper
½	cup dry white wine
½	cup low-sodium chicken broth
1	Tbsp finely grated lemon zest
½	cup finely grated Parmesan plus more for serving
¾	cup flat-leaf parsley, chopped
1	Tbsp tarragon, chopped
¼	cup chopped chives
2	Tbsp cold unsalted butter (optional)

1. Cook pasta per pkg. directions. Reserve 1 cup cooking liquid, then drain pasta and return to pot.

2. Meanwhile, heat oil in large skillet on medium. Add garlic and cook, stirring, until it starts to sizzle, about 1 minute.

3. Add chicken, season with red pepper flakes and ½ tsp each salt and pepper, and cook, breaking up into tiny pieces, until nearly cooked through, 4 to 5 min. Add wine and simmer until nearly evaporated, about 2 min.

4. Add broth and toss to combine, then bring to a simmer. Fold in lemon zest, Parmesan and herbs. Remove from heat and add butter if using, stirring and tossing until melted.

5. Toss with rigatoni and ½ cup reserved cooking liquid, adding more if pasta seems dry. Top with additional Parmesan if desired.

About 565 cal, 17 g fat (5 g sat), 6 g pro, 510 mg sodium, 68 g carb, 4 g fiber

**MAKE
IT AHEAD**
*Bolognese and pasta can
be refrigerated separately for
up to 4 days. When ready to
serve, bring a pot of water to a boil
and reheat pasta. Warm bolognese
in a skillet on medium. You can also
freeze the bolognese in an airtight
container for up to 3 months.
Thaw in the refrigerator
overnight.*

Cod in Parchment with Orange Leek Couscous

ACTIVE: 15 MIN. ✂ TOTAL: 30 MIN. ✂ SERVES 4

1 cup couscous

1 orange

1 leek, white and light green parts only, cut in half lengthwise, then sliced ½-in. thick

3 cups baby kale

1¼ lbs cod, cut into 4 portions

1 Tbsp olive oil

Kosher salt and pepper

1. Heat oven to 425°F. Tear off four 12-in. squares of parchment paper and arrange on two baking sheets. In a bowl, combine couscous with ¾ cup water.

2. Cut orange in half, then peel one half and coarsely chop fruit. Fold orange into couscous along with leek and baby kale.

3. Divide couscous mixture among pieces of parchment and top each with a piece of cod. Drizzle with oil and sprinkle with ½ tsp salt and ¼ tsp pepper, then squeeze remaining orange half over tops.

4. Cover each with another piece of parchment and fold each edge up and under three times, tucking edges underneath. Roast 12 min.

5. Transfer each packet to a plate. Using scissors or a knife, cut an "X" in the center and fold back the triangles.

About 340 cal, 5 g fat (1 g sat), 32 g pro, 330 mg sodium, 40 g carb, 3 g fiber

TEST KITCHEN TIP
If you are serving fewer people, this recipe can be easily cut in half or in 4. Just decrease the amounts of ingredients accordingly.

Beef Kofta with Kale and Chickpea Salad

ACTIVE: 20 MIN. ✂ TOTAL: 20 MIN. ✂ SERVES 4

1	lemon
1	lb ground beef
2	cloves garlic, finely chopped
1½	tsp ground cumin
1½	tsp ground coriander
	Kosher salt and pepper
3	Tbsp olive oil, divided
½	tsp dried oregano
1	small red onion, thinly sliced
1	15-oz can chickpeas, rinsed
4	cups baby kale
1	pint cherry tomatoes, halved if large

1. Finely grate zest of lemon and squeeze 3 Tbsp juice. In large bowl, combine beef, garlic, cumin, coriander, lemon zest, 1 Tbsp lemon juice and ½ tsp each salt and pepper. Form mixture into 12 flat ovals.

2. Heat 1 Tbsp oil in large skillet and cook kofta until browned and barely cooked through, 1½ to 2 min. per side.

3. In another large bowl, whisk oregano with remaining 2 Tbsp oil and remaining 2 Tbsp lemon juice. Add onion and chickpeas and toss to combine. Let sit 5 min., then toss with kale and tomatoes. Serve with kofta.

About 385 cal, 20 g fat (5 g sat), 29 g pro, 470 mg sodium, 23 g carb, 7 g fiber

MAKE IT AHEAD
Refrigerate cooked kofta in an airtight container for up to 3 days. Warm in a covered skillet on medium.

Summer Minestrone

ACTIVE: 25 MIN. ✂ TOTAL: 30 MIN. ✂ SERVES 4

1	Tbsp olive oil
1	large onion, finely chopped
	Kosher salt and pepper
2	cloves garlic, finely chopped
8	oz red potatoes, cut into ½-in. pieces
4	cups low-sodium vegetable broth
1	small zucchini, cut into ½-in. pieces
1	yellow squash, cut into ½-in. pieces
1	small carrot, thinly sliced
½	cup frozen peas
¼	cup grated Parmesan
1	cup fresh basil, roughly chopped

1. Heat oil in large saucepan on medium. Add onion, season with salt and pepper and cook, covered, stirring occasionally, 8 min.

2. Stir in garlic and cook 1 min. Add potatoes and vegetable broth and simmer 5 min. Add zucchini, squash and carrot; simmer 3 min.

3. Add peas and simmer until vegetables are just tender, 2 to 3 min.

4. Sprinkle with Parmesan and basil before serving.

About 185 cal, 6 g fat (1.5 g sat), 7 g pro, 490 mg sodium, 29 g carb, 5 g fiber

MAKE IT AHEAD
Refrigerate soup, without Parmesan and basil in airtight containers for up to 5 days. Warm as much as you need in a pot on medium-low in increments. Sprinkle with Parmesan and basil just before serving.

Pork with Roasted Asparagus and Apricot Relish

ACTIVE: 20 MIN. ✄ TOTAL: 25 MIN. ✄ SERVES 4

¼ cup dried apricots

½ cup white wine vinegar

3 Tbsp olive oil, divided

1¼ lbs pork tenderloin, trimmed and cut into 4 portions
Kosher salt and pepper

1 lb asparagus, trimmed

2 thin leeks (about 12 oz), white and light green parts only, sliced ¼-in. thick

1 tsp Dijon mustard

1 scallion, finely chopped

1. Heat oven to 450°F. Place apricots and vinegar in a small saucepan. Bring to a boil, boil 2 min., then remove from heat and let sit 10 min. Strain into a measuring cup; reserve apricots.

2. Meanwhile, heat 1 Tbsp oil in a large skillet on medium. Season pork with ½ tsp each salt and pepper and cook, turning occasionally, until golden brown on all sides and an instant-read thermometer inserted in center registers 145°F, 10 to 14 min. total. Transfer to a cutting board and let rest at least 5 min. before slicing.

3. While pork is cooking, on a large rimmed baking sheet, toss asparagus and leeks with 1 Tbsp oil and ¼ tsp each salt and pepper and roast until tender and beginning to brown at the edges, 12 to 15 min.

4. Finely chop apricots. In a small bowl, mix together mustard, 1 Tbsp apricot vinegar and remaining Tbsp oil. Stir in apricots and scallion. Serve over pork and vegetables.

About 285 cal, 12.5 g fat (2.5 g sat), 30 g pro, 465 mg sodium, 14 g carb, 3 g fiber

LOVE YOUR LEFTOVERS

Only slice as much pork as you need for dinner tonight. Store the remaining pork and any leftover vegetables separately in airtight containers for up to 3 days. You can slice and serve pork cold in sandwiches, cube and toss into salads or reheat then slice and serve warm. Reheat vegetables in a small skillet on medium.

Roasted Salmon with Charred Lemon Vinaigrette

ACTIVE: 20 MIN. ✂ TOTAL: 35 MIN. ✂ SERVES 4

1	lemon
2	bulbs fennel, thinly sliced
2	small red onions, thinly sliced
2½	Tbsp olive oil, divided
	Kosher salt and pepper
1¼	lbs skin-on salmon fillet
1	tsp stone-ground mustard
3	cups baby arugula

1. Heat broiler. Cut pointed ends off lemon, halve crosswise and place on a rimmed baking sheet, center cut sides up. Broil on top rack until charred, 5 min.; transfer to a plate and set aside.

2. Reduce oven temperature to 400°F. On rimmed baking sheet, toss fennel and onions with 1½ Tbsp oil and ¼ tsp each salt and pepper; arrange around edges of pan. Place salmon in center of pan and season with ¼ tsp each salt and pepper. Roast until vegetables are tender and salmon is opaque throughout, 17 to 20 min.

3. Juice charred lemon halves into a small bowl and whisk in mustard and remaining Tbsp oil. Remove baking sheet from oven and fold arugula into vegetables. Drizzle charred lemon vinaigrette over fish and vegetables and gently toss vegetables.

About 305 cal, 14 g fat (2.5 g sat), 31 g pro, 400 mg sodium, 14 g carb, 5 g fiber

LOVE YOUR LEFTOVERS
While this recipe can be halved, consider making all 4 servings. Refrigerate salmon and vegetables separately in airtight containers for up to 3 days. Flake salmon for salads or sandwiches and spoon vegetables on top of grain bowls or toss in hot pasta.

Skillet Pesto Chicken and Beans

ACTIVE: 15 MIN. ✂ TOTAL: 25 MIN. ✂ SERVES 4

8   small chicken thighs
    (about 2 lbs)
    Kosher salt and pepper
1   Tbsp olive oil
8   oz green beans, halved
1   cup cherry tomatoes
1   15-oz can butter beans,
    rinsed
2   Tbsp prepared pesto
    Grated Parmesan and
    chopped basil, for serving

1. Heat oven to 425°F. Season chicken thighs with ½ tsp each salt and pepper. Heat oil in large, oven-safe skillet on medium-high. Add chicken, skin sides down, and cook until golden brown, about 6 min.

2. Turn chicken over; add green beans, cherry tomatoes and butter beans and season with ¼ tsp salt. Roast until chicken is cooked through, 12 to 15 min.

3. Brush pesto over chicken and serve with grated Parmesan and chopped basil.

About 450 cal, 26 g fat (6.5 g sat), 38 g pro,
770 mg sodium, 22 g carb, 6 g fiber

Hummus-Stuffed Peppers

ACTIVE: 5 MIN. ✂ TOTAL: 5 MIN. ✂ SERVES 1

1   pepper
4   Tbsp hummus
2   Tbsp crumbled feta

Cut pepper in half and remove seeds. Spread hummus on each half and sprinkle with crumbled feta.

About 275 cal, 18 g fat (3 g sat fat), 12 g pro,
750 mg sodium, 22 g carb, 6 g fiber

LOVE YOUR LEFTOVERS

Shred chicken, discarding skin and bones. Refrigerate shredded chicken and vegetables separately for up to 3 days. Try warming veggies and serving for breakfast topped with a sunny-side up egg. And use shredded chicken for lunch salads, sandwiches or grain bowls.

WEEK 3 At-a-Glance

DAY 15

BREAKFAST
🕐 Shakshuka + 2 Slices Sprouted Grain Bread

LUNCH
Grilled Harissa Chicken Kebabs and Chickpea Salad

DINNER
Paprika Steak with Lentils and Spinach

SNACK
1 Medium Orange

DAY 16

BREAKFAST
🕐 Spinach and Pepper Mini Frittatas + 2 Slices Sprouted Grain Bread

LUNCH
Pesto Zucchini Orzo

DINNER
Roasted Garlicky Shrimp + 1 Whole-Grain Pita

SNACK
🕐 No-Bake Fruit and Nut Bar

DAY 17

BREAKFAST
🕐 Vegan Coconut Chia Pudding

LUNCH
🕐 Spiced Fresh Tomato Soup with Sweet and Herby Pitas

DINNER
🕐 Chicken and Broccoli Parchment + ½ cup Pesto Zucchini Orzo (Leftover)

SNACK
¼ cup Crunchy Chickpea Snacks

DAY 18

BREAKFAST
🕐 Classic Omelet and Greens

LUNCH
Salmon with Creamy Feta Cucumbers + 1 Whole-Grain Pita

DINNER
🕐 Quinoa Risotto with Arugula Mint Pesto

SNACK
Honey-Blueberry Oats

DAY 19

BREAKFAST
🕐 Grain Bowl with Sautéed Spinach

LUNCH
Summer Squash and Pecorino Pasta

DINNER
Apricot Grilled Pork Tenderloin and Peppers

SNACK
1 cup Lightly Salted Pistachios with Shells

DAY 20

BREAKFAST
🕐 Pumpkin Bread with Lemony Cream Cheese

LUNCH
🕐 Grilled Green Beans, Fennel and Farro + 4 oz Grilled Chicken Breast

DINNER
Paprika Chicken + Sautéed Spinach

SNACK
¼ cup Hummus + 10 Pita Chips

DAY 21

BREAKFAST
🕐 Classic Omelet and Greens

LUNCH
Spaghetti with No-Cook Tomato Sauce

DINNER
🕐 Salmon Burger with Spiced Sweet Potato Fries

SNACK
½ cup Fresh Veggie Crudités

WEEK 3: SHOPPING LIST

Check for leftover ingredients from Week 2 before purchasing new ingredients from the shopping list.

PRODUCE

Veggies
- 2 heads garlic
- 2 large yellow onions
- 2 small yellow onions
- 1½ red onions
- 3 medium shallots
- 4 small sweet potatoes (about 1½ lbs total)
- 1 1-in. piece ginger
- 1 small bulb fennel
- 7 small zucchini (4 to 5 oz each)
- 6 small yellow squash (4 to 5 oz each)
- 1¼ lbs broccoli
- ½ lb green beans
- ½ lb wax beans
- 1 lb seedless cucumbers
- 1 jalapeño
- 10 scallions
- 5 lbs tomatoes
- 1½ avocados
- ½ cup fresh veggie crudités

Greens & Lettuce
- 5 5-oz pkgs. baby spinach
- ½ cup packed arugula
- 2 (about 2 cups) large kale leaves
- 2 bunches spinach
- 1 cup radish or alfalfa sprouts
- ¼ cup microgreens

Herbs
- 1 cup flat-leaf parsley
- ¼ cup basil
- 2 Tbsp cilantro
- 1 cup mint
- 2 Tbsp fresh thyme

Fruit
- 5 lemons
- 1 medium orange
- ½ cup blueberries
- ½ cup fresh berries

MEAT & SEAFOOD
- 1¼ lbs boneless, skinless chicken breasts
- 8 6-oz boneless, skinless chicken breasts
- 4 oz grilled chicken breast
- 2 (about 1½ lbs total) 1-in.-thick strip steaks
- 2 small pork tenderloins (about ¾ lb each)
- 1¼ lbs skinless salmon fillets
- 4 5-oz skinless salmon fillets
- 1½ lbs large peeled and deveined shrimp

REFRIGERATED & DAIRY
- 27 large eggs
- 1½ cups 1% milk
- 1 cup almond or other nondairy milk
- ½ cup low-fat buttermilk
- ½ cup plain Greek yogurt
- ¼ cup nonfat plain Greek yogurt
- 3 Tbsp fresh goat cheese
- 1 oz Manchego cheese
- 7 oz feta
- 4 oz cream cheese
- 1 oz Parmesan
- 3 oz pecorino
- 1 oz ricotta salata
- ½ cup pesto
- ¼ cup hummus

BREAD & BAKERY
- 4 slices sprouted grain bread
- 4 buns
- 2 whole-grain pita
- 2 pocketless pitas

PANTRY

Oils, Vinegars, Condiments & Spices
- ½ cup white wine vinegar
- 1 tsp toasted sesame oil
- 1 Tbsp smoked paprika
- 1 Tbsp fennel seeds
- 1 tsp five-spice powder
- 1 12-oz jar roasted red peppers
- ¼ cup harissa pepper paste

Grains
- 12 oz rigatoni
- 12 oz whole-wheat spaghetti
- 8 oz orzo
- 1½ cups quinoa
- ½ cup quick-cooking farro
- 1 cup quick-cooking bulgur
- 2 cups cooked grains (such as farro, brown rice, quinoa)
- ½ cup old-fashioned oats

Beans & Veggies
- 1 cup dry lentils (we used black)
- 3 15-oz cans chickpeas

Broth & Wine
- 3 cups low-sodium chicken broth
- ¼ cup plus 2 Tbsp dry white wine

Baking
- 3 Tbsp plus 1 tsp honey
- 3 Tbsp agave syrup
- ½ tsp ground nutmeg
- 1 15-oz can pure pumpkin puree
- 1 14-oz can coconut milk

Nuts, Seeds & Fruits
- ½ cup toasted almonds
- 1 cup lightly salted pistachios with shells
- ¼ cup toasted pistachios
- 2 Tbsp pine nuts
- ¼ cup pepitas
- ½ cup black chia seeds
- ¼ cup apricot jam
- 2 Tbsp finely shredded unsweetened coconut

Chips
- 10 pita chips
- ¼ cup crunchy chickpea snacks

DAY 15

BREAKFAST

Shakshuka (p. 48) + 2 Slices
Sprouted Grain Bread

LUNCH

Grilled Harissa Chicken
Kebabs and Chickpea Salad
(p. 130)

DINNER

Paprika Steak with Lentils
and Spinach (p. 144)

SNACK

1 Medium Orange

NOTES TO SELF

_____
_____
_____
_____
_____
_____
_____
_____
_____
_____
_____
_____
_____
_____
_____
_____
_____
_____

WATER

☐ ☐ ☐ ☐ ☐ ☐ ☐ ☐

MOVEMENT/WORKOUT Y ☐ N ☐
ACTIVITY: _____
_____

DURATION: _____
_____

INTENSITY: _____
_____

SLEEP
Bedtime Last Night: _____ : _____
Wake Time This Morning: _____ : _____

_____
_____
_____
_____

MOOD

☺ ☒ ☹

_____
_____
_____

CONNECTION

_____
_____
_____

DAY 16

BREAKFAST

Spinach and Pepper Mini
Frittatas (2 Servings) (p. 42) +
2 Slices Sprouted
Grain Bread

LUNCH

Pesto Zucchini Orzo (p. 132)

DINNER

Roasted Garlicky Shrimp
(p. 146) + 1 Whole-Grain Pita

SNACK

No-Bake Fruit and Nut Bar
(p. 46)

NOTES TO SELF

WATER

MOVEMENT/WORKOUT Y ☐ N ☐
ACTIVITY: _____

DURATION: _____

INTENSITY: _____

SLEEP
Bedtime Last Night: _____ : _____
Wake Time This Morning: _____ : _____

MOOD
☺ ☺ ☹

CONNECTION

DAY 17

BREAKFAST
Vegan Coconut Chia Pudding
(1 cup) (p. 44)

LUNCH
Spiced Fresh Tomato Soup
with Sweet and Herby Pitas
(p. 134)

DINNER
Chicken and Broccoli Parch-
ment (p. 148) + ½ cup Pesto
Zucchini Orzo (Leftover)

SNACK
¼ cup Crunchy
Chickpea Snacks

NOTES TO SELF

_____
_____
_____
_____
_____
_____
_____
_____
_____
_____
_____
_____
_____
_____

WATER

MOVEMENT/WORKOUT Y ☐ N ☐
ACTIVITY: _____
_____
_____
DURATION: _____
_____
INTENSITY: _____
_____

SLEEP
Bedtime Last Night: _____ : _____
Wake Time This Morning: _____ : _____
_____
_____
_____

MOOD
☺   😐   ☹
_____
_____
_____

CONNECTION
_____
_____
_____
_____

DAY 18

BREAKFAST
Classic Omelet and Greens
(p. 88)

LUNCH
Salmon with Creamy Feta
Cucumbers (p. 136)
+ 1 Whole-Grain Pita

DINNER
Quinoa Risotto with Arugula
Mint Pesto (p. 150)

SNACK
Honey-Blueberry Oats (p. 77)

NOTES TO SELF

_____
_____
_____
_____
_____
_____
_____
_____
_____
_____
_____
_____
_____

WATER

MOVEMENT/WORKOUT Y ☐ N ☐
ACTIVITY: _____
_____

DURATION: _____
_____

INTENSITY: _____
_____

SLEEP
Bedtime Last Night: _____ : _____
Wake Time This Morning: _____ : _____
_____
_____
_____

MOOD
☺ 😐 ☹

_____
_____

CONNECTION
_____
_____
_____
_____

DAY 19

BREAKFAST
Grain Bowl with Sautéed
Spinach (p. 92)

LUNCH
Summer Squash and Pecorino
Pasta (p. 138)

DINNER
Apricot Grilled Pork Tenderloin and Peppers (p. 152)

SNACK
1 cup Lightly Salted Pistachios with Shells

NOTES TO SELF

WATER

MOVEMENT/WORKOUT Y ☐ N ☐
ACTIVITY: _____

DURATION: _____

INTENSITY: _____

SLEEP
Bedtime Last Night: _____ : _____
Wake Time This Morning: _____ : _____

MOOD
☺ ☺ ☹

CONNECTION

BREAKFAST

Pumpkin Bread with Lemony
Cream Cheese (p. 128)

LUNCH

Grilled Green Beans, Fennel
and Farro (p. 140) + 4 oz
Grilled Chicken Breast

DINNER

Paprika Chicken (p. 154)
+ Sautéed Spinach (about
4 cups with 1 Tbsp olive oil
and 1 clove garlic)

SNACK

¼ cup Hummus
+ 10 Pita Chips

NOTES TO SELF

_____
_____
_____
_____
_____
_____
_____
_____
_____
_____
_____
_____
_____

WATER

☐ ☐ ☐ ☐ ☐ ☐ ☐ ☐

MOVEMENT/WORKOUT Y ☐ N ☐
ACTIVITY: _____
_____

DURATION: _____
_____

INTENSITY: _____
_____

SLEEP

Bedtime Last Night: _____ : _____
Wake Time This Morning: _____ : _____

_____
_____
_____

MOOD

☺ 😐 ☹

_____

CONNECTION

_____
_____
_____
_____

DAY 21

BREAKFAST
Classic Omelet and Greens
(p. 88)

LUNCH
Spaghetti with No-Cook
Tomato Sauce (p. 142)

DINNER
Salmon Burger with Spiced
Sweet Potato Fries (p. 156)

SNACK
½ cup Fresh Veggie Crudités

NOTES TO SELF

WATER

MOVEMENT/WORKOUT Y ☐ N ☐
ACTIVITY: _____

DURATION: _____

INTENSITY: _____

SLEEP
Bedtime Last Night: _____ : _____
Wake Time This Morning: _____ : _____

MOOD
☺ ☺ ☹

CONNECTION

RECIPES

Pumpkin Bread with Lemony Cream Cheese

ACTIVE: 25 MIN. ✄ TOTAL: 1 HR. 25 MIN. ✄ SERVES 10

3	cups whole-wheat flour
1½	tsp kosher salt
1	tsp black pepper
1	tsp baking soda
½	tsp baking powder
½	tsp ground nutmeg
1	15-oz can pure pumpkin puree
½	cup low-fat buttermilk
6	Tbsp olive oil
2	Tbsp dark brown sugar
2	Tbsp chopped fresh thyme
3	large eggs
1	small zucchini, grated and squeezed of excess moisture
2	large kale leaves, stems discarded, leaves chopped (about 2 cups)
	Raw pepitas (optional)
	Lemony Cream Cheese (see right)

1. Heat oven to 350°F. Coat 8½- by 4½-in. loaf pan with nonstick cooking spray; set aside.

2. In bowl, whisk together flour, salt, pepper, baking soda, baking powder and nutmeg. In large bowl, whisk together pumpkin, buttermilk, oil, sugar, thyme and eggs. Stir flour mixture into pumpkin mixture until just combined. Fold in zucchini and kale and transfer to prepared pan; sprinkle with pepitas if using.

3. Bake until wooden pick inserted in a few places comes out clean, 60 to 75 min. Cool in pan on wire rack 10 min., then transfer to rack to cool completely.

4. Make the Lemony Cream Cheese: In bowl, mix together 4 oz softened cream cheese, ¼ cup nonfat plain Greek yogurt, 1 tsp each grated lemon zest and fresh lemon juice and ¼ tsp each kosher salt and pepper.

Per slice with 1 Tbsp spread about 292 cal, 14 g fat (4 g sat), 9 g pro, 553 mg sodium, 35 g carb, 5 g fiber

MAKE IT AHEAD

Tightly wrap bread and store at room temperature for up to 4 days. Refrigerate spread in an airtight container for up to 4 days.

Grilled Harissa Chicken Kebabs and Chickpea Salad

ACTIVE: 20 MIN. ✷ TOTAL: 20 MIN. ✷ SERVES 4

1   cup quick-cooking bulgur
¼   cup harissa pepper paste
2   Tbsp olive oil
2   Tbsp honey
1¼   lbs boneless, skinless
     chicken breasts,
     cut into small pieces
1   15-oz can chickpeas,
     rinsed
¾   cup finely chopped
     fresh parsley
     Kosher salt

1. Cook bulgur per pkg. directions. Heat grill to medium-high.

2. In large bowl, whisk harissa with olive oil and honey; set half aside for serving.

3. To remaining harissa mixture, add chicken and toss to coat, then thread onto skewers. Grill, turning once, until cooked through, 6 to 8 min.

4. Toss chickpeas with bulgur, parsley and ½ tsp salt. Divide among plates and top with chicken skewers. Serve drizzled with remaining olive oil and honey mixture .

About 495 cal, 13 g fat (2 g sat), 39 g pro, 560 mg sodium, 57 g carb, 13 g fiber

LOVE YOUR LEFTOVERS

Refrigerate chickpea salad and chicken (remove from skewers) in separate containers for up to 3 days. Try tossing leftover chickpea mixture with arugula, squeezing on lemon juice for an easy salad. Chicken can be used for salads, sandwiches or grain bowls.

Pesto Zucchini Orzo

ACTIVE: 15 MIN. ✂ TOTAL: 30 MIN. ✂ SERVES 4

8	oz orzo
1	Tbsp olive oil
¼	cup white wine vinegar
	Kosher salt and pepper
2	small zucchini (about 4 oz each), very thinly sliced
2	small yellow squash (about 4 oz each), very thinly sliced
½	cup store-bought pesto
¼	cup toasted almonds, chopped

1. Cook orzo per pkg. directions. Drain well, then transfer to large bowl; toss with oil.

2. Meanwhile, in another large bowl, whisk together vinegar and ¼ tsp each salt and pepper. Add zucchini and squash and toss to combine. Let sit until orzo is done, at least 5 min.

3. With slotted spoon, transfer vegetables to bowl with orzo, reserving vinegar in bowl, and toss to combine.

4. Whisk pesto into vinegar, then drizzle over orzo and sprinkle with almonds.

About 445 cal, 22 g fat (3.5 g sat), 14 g pro, 315 mg sodium, 51 g carb, 4 g fiber

MAKE IT AHEAD
Prepare the grains and veggies and refrigerate separately in an airtight container for up to 2 days. Reheat, covered, in a small skillet on medium-low or microwave in 20-second increments. Top with vinegar mixture before serving.

Spiced Fresh Tomato Soup with Sweet and Herby Pitas

ACTIVE: 25 MIN. ⁙ TOTAL: 25 MIN. ⁙ SERVES 4

FOR SOUP

2 Tbsp olive oil
1 large onion, chopped
1 large red pepper, chopped
½ tsp salt
2 cloves garlic
1 jalapeño
1 1-in. piece ginger
2 tsp ground coriander
1 tsp ground cumin
2½ lbs tomatoes, roughly chopped
2½ cups water
2 pocketless pitas

FOR TOPPING

1 Tbsp brown sugar
2 Tbsp butter or olive oil
2 Tbsp finely shredded unsweetened coconut
2 Tbsp cilantro

1. Make soup: Heat large Dutch oven on medium-low. Add olive oil, onion, red pepper and salt, and cook, covered, stirring occasionally, until tender, 8 to 10 min.

2. Meanwhile, finely grate garlic, jalapeño and ginger. Add to onion and cook, stirring, 1 min. Stir in coriander and cumin and cook 1 min.

3. Add tomatoes and water; increase heat and simmer, partially covered, 10 min. While tomatoes are cooking, toast 2 pocketless pitas.

4. Using immersion blender (or standard blender, in batches), puree soup until smooth.

5. Make topping: Combine brown sugar, butter, coconut and cilantro in bowl. Spread onto toasted pitas, then cut and serve with soup.

About 325 cal, 16 g fat (6.5 g sat), 6 g pro, 565 mg sodium, 43 g carb, 7 g fiber

**MAKE
IT AHEAD**
*Refrigerate soup in
airtight containers for up
to 3 days or freeze for up to
3 months. If frozen, thaw in
refrigerator overnight. Warm
in a pot over medium heat
and puree again
before serving.*

Salmon with Creamy Feta Cucumbers

ACTIVE: 20 MIN. · TOTAL: 20 MIN. · SERVES 4

- 1 Tbsp olive oil
- 2 lemons
- 4 5-oz skinless salmon fillets
- Kosher salt and pepper
- 1 lb seedless cucumbers, sliced on a bias
- 3 oz feta cheese
- 1/4 cup plain Greek yogurt
- 1/4 cup small mint leaves, roughly chopped

LOVE YOUR LEFTOVERS
Refrigerate salmon and cucumber salad (without mint) separately in airtight containers for up to 2 days.

1. Heat oil in a large skillet on medium. Halve 1 lemon and place halves, cut sides down, in the skillet. Season salmon with ½ tsp each salt and pepper and cook until golden brown and opaque throughout, 3 to 6 min. per side. Transfer salmon fillets to plates. Transfer lemon halves to a cutting board and cut each in half.

2. Meanwhile, in a large bowl, toss cucumbers with ¼ tsp salt. Finely grate zest of remaining lemon into a food processor and squeeze in 3 Tbsp juice. Add feta and yogurt and puree until smooth.

3. Toss with cucumbers to coat, then fold in mint and freshly cracked pepper. Serve with salmon and a charred lemon wedge for squeezing.

About 280 cal, 12.5 g fat (5 g sat), 34 g pro, 635 mg sodium, 9 g carb, 1 g fiber

Summer Squash and Pecorino Pasta

ACTIVE: 15 MIN. ⁘ TOTAL: 25 MIN. ⁘ SERVES 4

- 12 oz rigatoni
- 2 Tbsp olive oil
- 1 shallot, halved and thinly sliced
- 1½ lbs zucchini and summer squash (about 4 small), thinly sliced into half-moons
- Kosher salt and pepper
- 3 oz pecorino cheese (about 1 cup), grated plus more for serving
- ⅓ cup mint, thinly sliced
- 1 Tbsp lemon juice

1. Cook pasta per pkg. directions. Reserve ¾ cup cooking liquid then drain.

2. Meanwhile, heat oil in large, deep skillet on medium. Cook shallot, stirring occasionally, until golden brown, 3 to 4 min. Add zucchini and squash and ½ tsp each salt and pepper and cook, tossing occasionally, until squash is very tender but still holds its shape, 10 to 12 min.

3. Add pasta to skillet and toss with squash and cheese, adding reserved cooking liquid 2 Tbsp at a time, to form a sauce that coats pasta. Fold in mint and lemon juice. Top with additional cheese and black pepper if desired.

About 490 cal, 13.5 g fat (5 g sat), 21 g pro, 505 mg sodium, 71 g carb, 5 g fiber

Grilled Green Beans, Fennel and Farro

ACTIVE: 20 MIN. ✄ TOTAL: 25 MIN. ✄ SERVES 4

½ cup quick-cooking farro
½ lb green beans, trimmed
½ lb wax beans, trimmed
2 Tbsp olive oil, divided
   Kosher salt
1 Tbsp fennel seeds
   Pinch red pepper flakes
2 Tbsp white wine vinegar
1 tsp honey
¼ cup toasted pistachios,
   chopped
1 small bulb fennel, very
   thinly shaved
   Fennel fronds, for serving

1. Heat grill to medium-high. Cook farro per pkg. directions. Drain, transfer to large bowl, and let cool to room temperature.

2. In second large bowl, toss green and wax beans with ½ Tbsp oil and ¼ tsp salt. Grill, turning occasionally, until just tender, 4 to 6 min. Transfer to bowl with farro.

3. In small skillet on medium, toast fennel seeds and pepper flakes until fragrant. Let cool, then pulse in spice grinder (or crush with side of heavy skillet) until mostly cracked.

4. While spices are cooling, in small bowl, whisk together vinegar, honey, remaining 1½ Tbsp oil and ¼ tsp salt. Stir in fennel seed mixture and pistachios. Toss farro and beans with dressing and fold in fennel. Serve topped with fennel fronds if desired.

About 230 cal, 11 g fat (1.5 g sat), 7 g pro,
450 mg sodium, 30 g carb, 7 g fiber

MAKE IT AHEAD
Prepare salad without pistachios and refrigerate in an airtight container for up to 3 days. Toss with pistachios just before serving.

Spaghetti with No-Cook Tomato Sauce

ACTIVE: 20 MIN. ✖ TOTAL: 30 MIN. ✖ SERVES 4

1	lb tomatoes (about 5)
¼	cup olive oil
	Kosher salt and
	black pepper
12	oz whole-wheat spaghetti
2	cloves garlic, crushed
¾	tsp crushed red pepper
¼	cup roasted almonds,
	coarsely chopped
¼	cup chopped fresh basil
2	Tbsp chopped
	fresh parsley
1	oz ricotta salata, shaved
	with peeler (about ½ cup)

1. Finely chop 4 tomatoes; transfer to large bowl with olive oil and ¼ tsp salt.

2. Cook spaghetti per pkg. directions. Reserve ¼ cup cooking liquid; drain pasta.

3. Meanwhile, chop remaining tomato. Place in food processor along with garlic, red pepper, 3 Tbsp almonds and ½ tsp salt; puree until smooth. Stir into bowl with tomatoes.

4. Add cooked spaghetti, basil and parsley; toss, adding some reserved cooking liquid if needed. Divide pasta among serving bowls. Top with cheese and remaining almonds.

About 600 cal, 29 g fat (4 g sat), 18 g pro, 610 mg sodium, 77 g carb, 12 g fiber

Paprika Steak with Lentils and Spinach

ACTIVE: 30 MIN. ✖ **TOTAL: 30 MIN.** ✖ **SERVES 4**

3   Tbsp olive oil
1   clove garlic, finely
    chopped
1   cup dry lentils
    (we used black)
¼   cup dry white wine
3   cups low-sodium
    chicken broth
2   1 in. thick strip steaks
    (about 1½ lbs total)
1   Tbsp smoked paprika plus
    more for serving
    Kosher salt and pepper
1   5-oz pkg. baby spinach
    Greek yogurt and
    chopped flat-leaf parsley,
    for serving

1. In a medium saucepan, heat 1 Tbsp oil and garlic on medium until garlic is sizzling on the edges. Add lentils and toss to coat. Add wine and simmer 2 min. Add broth, partially cover, and bring to a boil, then reduce heat and simmer until tender, 20 to 22 min.

2. Meanwhile, pat steaks dry with a paper towel, then rub with paprika and ½ tsp each salt and pepper; shake off any excess. Heat 1 Tbsp oil in a large skillet on medium and cook to desired doneness, 4 to 5 min. per side for medium-rare. Transfer to a cutting board and let rest at least 5 min. before slicing.

3. Discard any excess liquid from lentils, then fold in spinach, remaining Tbsp oil and ¼ tsp each salt and pepper.

4. Serve steak with lentils. Dollop with yogurt and sprinkle with paprika and parsley if desired.

About 575 cal, 24.5 g fat (7.5 g sat), 54 g pro, 520 mg sodium, 36 g carb, 11 g fiber

LOVE YOUR LEFTOVERS
Slice only the steak you plan on eating at this meal. Refrigerate remaining steak and lentils in separate containers for up to 3 days. For an easy lunch, spread yogurt in a pita pocket. Thinly slice steak and add to pita along with any leftover lentils and some mixed greens or arugula, if desired.

Roasted Garlicky Shrimp

ACTIVE: 10 MIN. ✂ TOTAL: 20 MIN. ✂ SERVES 4

1½ lbs large peeled and
    deveined shrimp
1   12-oz jar roasted red
    peppers, drained and cut
    into 1-in. pieces
4   scallions, sliced
2   cloves garlic, pressed
2   Tbsp dry white wine
1   Tbsp fresh lemon juice
    Kosher salt and pepper
2   Tbsp olive oil
4   oz feta cheese, crumbled
    Pitas and baby spinach,
    rice or couscous, or salad
    greens, for serving

1. Heat oven to 425°F. In 1½- to 2-quart baking dish, combine shrimp, red peppers, scallions, garlic, wine, lemon juice and ¼ tsp each salt and pepper.

2. Drizzle with olive oil and sprinkle with feta cheese. Bake until shrimp are opaque throughout, 12 to 15 min. Spoon into pitas along with baby spinach, serve over rice or couscous or toss with your favorite salad greens.

About 285 cal, 14.5 g fat (5.5 g sat), 28 g pro, 1,465 mg sodium, 9 g carb, 3 g fiber

Chicken and Broccoli Parchment

ACTIVE: 35 MIN. ✂ TOTAL: 45 MIN. ✂ SERVES 4

1¼ lbs broccoli, stems sliced,
    crowns cut into
    small florets
2   cloves garlic, pressed
2   Tbsp olive oil, divided
    Kosher salt and pepper
4   6-oz boneless, skinless
    chicken breasts
½   small red onion,
    finely chopped
1   lemon
8   oz tomatoes, chopped

1. Heat oven to 400°F. Toss broccoli with garlic, 1 Tbsp oil and ¼ tsp each salt and pepper. Divide among four 12-in. squares of parchment. Season chicken with ¼ tsp each salt and pepper and place on top of broccoli. Cover with second piece of parchment and fold up edges to seal. Place packets on 2 rimmed baking sheets and roast 15 min.

2. Meanwhile, finely grate zest of lemon and squeeze 2 Tbsp juice. In medium bowl, combine onion, lemon juice, remaining Tbsp oil and ¼ tsp each salt and pepper. Let sit 4 min., then toss with tomatoes. Cut open packets; top with vinaigrette and lemon zest.

About 330 cal, 12 g fat (2 g sat), 43 g pro,
485 mg sodium, 14 g carb, 5 g fiber

MAKE
IT AHEAD

Only assemble the packets
you plan on eating at this meal.
To get ahead you can create
parchment packets with just chicken
and just broccoli, then cook, let cool and
refrigerate separately in airtight
containers for up to 3 days. Refrigerate
any leftover vinaigrette for up to
1 day. All of these ingredients are
great served over your
favorite grain or tossed
with greens.

Quinoa Risotto with Arugula Mint Pesto

ACTIVE: 30 MIN. ✄ TOTAL: 40 MIN. ✄ SERVES 4

½ cup packed arugula

⅓ cup grated Manchego cheese (about 1 oz)

¼ cup packed fresh mint leaves plus more for garnish

2 garlic cloves

1 Tbsp pine nuts, toasted, plus more for garnish
  Kosher salt

¼ cup olive oil plus 2 tsp

2 medium shallots, chopped

1½ cups quinoa, rinsed and drained

2 Tbsp butter

2 Tbsp fresh lemon juice

1 15-oz can garbanzo beans, rinsed and drained
  Microgreens, for garnish

1. In food processor, pulse arugula, Manchego, mint, garlic, pine nuts and ¼ tsp salt until finely chopped, scraping down sides as needed. Transfer to a medium bowl; stir in ¼ cup oil.

2. In a 4-quart saucepan, heat remaining 2 tsp oil on medium. Add shallots; cook 2 min., stirring occasionally. Add quinoa; cook 1 minute, stirring. Add 2 cups warm water and ½ tsp salt and bring to a boil on high. Reduce heat; simmer until most of water is absorbed, stirring occasionally, 6 to 8 min. Add another 2 cups warm water; simmer until quinoa is just tender, stirring occasionally, 15 to 18 min.

3. Add butter, lemon juice, half of pesto and ½ cup water to quinoa, stirring to combine. Fold in beans. Divide quinoa mixture among 4 serving bowls and spoon remaining pesto over quinoa. Garnish with microgreens, additional mint and pine nuts, if desired.

About 585 cal, 31 g fat (8 g sat), 17 g pro, 615 mg sodium, 62 g carb, 10 g fiber

MAKE IT AHEAD
Prepare quinoa and pesto, but do not combine. Refrigerate both separately in airtight containers for up to 2 days. Warm quinoa, toss with pesto and top with greens, herbs and pine nuts as directed.

Apricot Grilled Pork Tenderloin and Peppers

ACTIVE: 25 MIN. ✂ TOTAL: 25 MIN. ✂ SERVES 4

4	peppers (red, yellow or a combination), quartered
1	red onion, cut into ½-in. wedges
1	Tbsp oil
	Kosher salt and pepper
2	small pork tenderloins, about ¾ lb each
¼	cup apricot jam
2	Tbsp white wine vinegar

1. Heat grill on medium-high. Toss peppers and red onion with oil and season with salt and pepper.

2. Season pork tenderloins with ¼ tsp each salt and pepper. Grill vegetables and pork, covered, turning occasionally, until vegetables are tender, 8 to 10 min. Transfer vegetables to cutting board.

3. Mix apricot jam and white wine vinegar in a bowl. Continue grilling pork, basting with sauce until cooked through (145°F), 3 to 6 min. Let rest 5 min. before slicing. Coarsely chop peppers and serve with onion, pork and any remaining sauce.

About 320 cal, 9 g fat (2.5 g sat), 36 g pro, 335 mg sodium, 23 g carb, 3 g fiber

Paprika Chicken

ACTIVE: 15 MIN. ⁘ TOTAL: 20 MIN. ⁘ SERVES 4

- 12 oz tomatoes
- 8 cloves garlic, smashed, in their skins
- 1 15-oz can chickpeas, rinsed
- 3 Tbsp olive oil, divided
- Kosher salt and pepper
- 4 6-oz boneless, skinless chicken breasts
- 2 tsp paprika

Heat oven to 425°F. On rimmed baking sheet, toss tomatoes, garlic and chickpeas with 2 Tbsp oil and ¼ tsp each salt and pepper. Roast 10 min. Heat remaining Tbsp oil in large skillet on medium. Season chicken with paprika and ½ tsp each salt and pepper and cook until golden brown on one side, 5 to 6 min. Flip and cook 1 min. more. Transfer to baking sheet with tomatoes and chickpeas and roast until cooked through, 6 min. more. Before serving, discard garlic skins.

About 390 cal, 16 g fat (2.5 g sat), 40 g pro, 590 mg sodium, 21 g carb, 6 g fiber

Salmon Burgers with Spiced Sweet Potato Fries

ACTIVE: 30 MIN. ✂ TOTAL: 30 MIN. ✂ SERVES 4

4   small sweet potatoes
    (about 1½ lbs total), cut
    into ½-in.-thick wedges
3   Tbsp olive oil, divided
1   tsp five-spice powder
    Kosher salt
1¼ lbs skinless salmon fillet,
    cut into 1-in. pieces
2   Tbsp low-sodium
    soy sauce
1   tsp toasted sesame oil
2   scallions, thinly sliced
4   buns, toasted
1   avocado, thinly sliced
1   cup radish or alfalfa
    sprouts

1. Heat oven to 450°F. On rimmed baking sheet, toss potatoes with 2 Tbsp oil, then five-spice powder and ¼ tsp salt. Transfer half to second baking sheet and arrange all in single layer. Roast until crisp, 20 to 25 min.

2. Meanwhile, in food processor, pulse salmon, soy sauce and sesame oil 4 to 5 times, just until coarsely chopped. Add scallions and pulse to combine. Form mixture into four ¾-in.-thick patties.

3. Heat remaining Tbsp oil in large nonstick skillet on medium and cook patties, turning once (do not flatten), until opaque throughout, 2 to 3 min. per side. Transfer to buns and top with avocado and sprouts. Serve with sweet potato fries.

About 675 cal, 37 g fat (5.5 g sat), 37 g pro, 735 mg sodium, 50 g carb, 9 g fiber

MAKE IT AHEAD

Prepare salmon patties but only cook what you plan to eat. Tightly wrap and refrigerate others for up to 1 day. Refrigerate roasted sweet potatoes in an airtight container for up to 3 days. You can use any leftovers or make a double batch and use in breakfast burritos, on grain bowls or tossed in salad.

WEEK 4 At-a-Glance

DAY 22

BREAKFAST
🕐 Pumpkin Bread with Lemony Cream Cheese

LUNCH
Shrimp Bowls with Scallion Vinaigrette

DINNER
Grilled Moroccan Steak and Carrots

SNACK
1 Large Apple with Cinnamon

DAY 23

BREAKFAST
🕐 Vegan Coconut Chia Pudding

LUNCH
🕐 Cucumber and Cantaloupe Quinoa Salad

DINNER
Grilled Leek, Zucchini and Ricotta Pizza

SNACKS
½ cup Fresh Veggie Crudités

DAY 24

BREAKFAST
🕐 Spinach and Pepper Mini Frittatas + 2 Slices Sprouted Grain Bread

LUNCH
Grilled Sweet Potatoes with Lemon-Herb Sauce + 4 oz Grilled Chicken

DINNER
Chicken and Asparagus Ribbons with Meyer Lemon Vinaigrette

SNACK
Strawberry-Almond Oats

DAY 25

BREAKFAST
Blueberry-Banana-Nut Smoothie

LUNCH
Tomato, Peach and Basil Salad + 4 oz Grilled Chicken

DINNER
Pork with Grilled Sweet Potato Fries

SNACK
½ cup Crunchy Chickpeas Snacks

DAY 26

BREAKFAST
Nectarine Bruschetta

LUNCH
Charred Shrimp, Leek and Asparagus Skewers

DINNER
Harissa Sirloin with Couscous Salad

SNACK
2 Tbsp Hummus + 10 Pita Chips

DAY 27

BREAKFAST
🕐 Classic Omelet and Greens + 2 Slices Sprouted Grain Bread

LUNCH
Chicken Cutlet Sandwiches

DINNER
🕐 Grilled Ratatouille Linguine

SNACK
Hummus-Stuffed Peppers

DAY 28

BREAKFAST
Strawberry-Almond Oats

LUNCH
Grilled Eggplant with Chickpea Croutons + Mixed Greens Side Salad

DINNER
Roasted Chicken and Garlic Potatoes with Red Pepper Relish

SNACK
1 5.3-oz Container Low-Sugar Flavored Greek Yogurt

Check for leftover ingredients from Week 3 before purchasing new ingredients from the shopping list.

PRODUCE

Veggies
- 8 cloves garlic
- 2 small yellow onions
- 1 red onion
- 2 small red onions
- 2 lbs small, thin carrots
- 3 large sweet potatoes
- 2 lbs sweet potatoes
- 1½ lbs (about 24) golden new potatoes
- 3 leeks (1 large, 2 medium)
- 1 Tbsp finely grated fresh ginger
- 2 large zucchini
- 2 small zucchini
- 2 medium eggplants (12 oz each)
- 1 small eggplant
- 1 lb broccoli
- 2 lbs asparagus (1 lb thick and 1 lb thin)
- 3 large red peppers
- 1 yellow pepper
- 1 small fresno chile
- 1 small jalapeño
- 6 scallions (about 1 bunch)
- 1 Persian cucumber
- 8 oz plum tomatoes
- 1 lb heirloom tomatoes
- 1 avocado

Greens & Lettuce
- 3 5-oz pkgs. baby spinach
- 1 5-oz pkg. plus 2 cups mixed greens
- 2 cups baby arugula
- ½ cup fresh veggie crudités

Herbs
- 1¾ cups flat-leaf parsley
- 1½ cups cilantro
- 2 cups mint leaves
- ½ cup basil leaves
- 2 Tbsp chopped chives

Fruit
- 7 lemons
- 1 Meyer lemon
- 1 cup strawberries
- ¼ to ½ cup fresh berries
- 1 banana
- 1 large apple
- ½ (about 1½ lbs) small cantaloupe
- 1 lb yellow peaches or nectarines
- 1 nectarine

MEAT & SEAFOOD
- 2½ lbs boneless, skinless chicken breasts
- 4 6-oz boneless, skinless chicken breasts
- 8 oz grilled chicken
- 2¼ lbs sirloin steak
- 4 bone-in pork chops
- 2 lbs large (21- to 25-count) peeled and deveined shrimp

REFRIGERATED & DAIRY
- 2½ cups 1% milk
- 2 cups almond milk
- 11 large eggs
- ¼ cup plain Greek yogurt
- ¼ cup plain full-fat yogurt
- 1 5.3-oz container low-sugar flavored Greek yogurt
- 1 oz pecorino (¼ cup grated)
- 1 oz Parmesan (about ¼ cup)
- 2 cups plus 6 Tbsp ricotta cheese
- 4 oz feta
- 2 Tbsp crumbled feta
- 3 Tbsp fresh goat cheese
- ½ oz ricotta salata
- 1 lb pizza dough
- 6 Tbsp hummus

FROZEN
- ½ cup frozen blueberries

BREAD & BAKERY
- 4 slices sprouted grain bread
- 2 large thick slices country bread
- 4 5-in. pieces baguette

PANTRY

Oils, Vinegars, Condiments & Spices
- 2 Tbsp red wine vinegar
- 2 Tbsp white wine vinegar
- 3 Tbsp sherry vinegar
- 1 Tbsp rice vinegar
- 1 Tbsp champagne vinegar
- 1 tsp Dijon mustard
- ½ cup mayonnaise
- 1 tsp smoked paprika
- 2½ Tbsp harissa paste
- 2 Tbsp olive oil & lemon vinaigrette

Grains
- 12 oz linguine
- 1½ cups quinoa
- ½ cup tricolor quinoa
- 1 cup couscous

Beans & Veggies
- ¾ cup roasted red peppers
- 1 Tbsp capers

Broth & Wine
- 3 cups low-sodium chicken broth
- ¼ cup plus 2 Tbsp dry white wine

Baking
- 7 Tbsp plus 1 tsp honey
- 3 Tbsp agave syrup
- 1 14-oz can coconut milk
- 1½ cups old-fashioned oats
- 1 cup chickpea flour

Nuts, Seeds & Fruits
- ⅓ cup plus ¼ cup roasted almonds
- ¼ cup sliced almonds
- ⅓ cup walnuts
- ¼ cup pepitas
- 2 Tbsp almond butter
- 2 Tbsp toasted sesame seeds
- 2 Tbsp hemp seed
- ½ cup black chia seeds

Chips
- 10 pita chips
- ½ cup crunchy chickpea snacks

DAY 22

BREAKFAST

Pumpkin Bread with Lemony
Cream Cheese (p. 128)

LUNCH

Shrimp Bowls with
Scallion Vinaigrette (p. 170)

DINNER

Grilled Moroccan Steak
and Carrots (p. 184)

SNACK

1 Large Apple with Cinnamon

NOTES TO SELF

WATER

MOVEMENT/WORKOUT Y ☐ N ☐
ACTIVITY: _____

DURATION: _____

INTENSITY: _____

SLEEP
Bedtime Last Night: _____ : _____
Wake Time This Morning: _____ : _____

MOOD
☺ ☺ ☹

CONNECTION

BREAKFAST

Vegan Coconut Chia Pudding
(1 cup) (p. 44)

LUNCH

Cucumber and Cantaloupe
Quinoa Salad (p. 172)

DINNER

Grilled Leek, Zucchini and
Ricotta Pizza (p. 186)

SNACK

½ cup Fresh Veggie Crudités

NOTES TO SELF

WATER

MOVEMENT/WORKOUT Y ☐ N ☐

ACTIVITY. _____

DURATION: _____

INTENSITY: _____

SLEEP

Bedtime Last Night: _____ : _____
Wake Time This Morning: _____ : _____

MOOD

☺ ☻ ☹

CONNECTION

DAY 24

BREAKFAST

Spinach and Pepper Mini
Frittatas (2 Servings) (p. 42)
+ 2 Slices Sprouted
Grain Bread

LUNCH

Grilled Sweet Potatoes with
Lemon-Herb Sauce (p. 174)
+ 4 oz Grilled Chicken

DINNER

Chicken and Asparagus
Ribbons with Meyer
Lemon Vinaigrette (p. 188)

SNACK

Strawberry-Almond Oats
(p. 92)

NOTES TO SELF

WATER

MOVEMENT/WORKOUT Y ☐ N ☐
ACTIVITY: _____

DURATION: _____

INTENSITY: _____

SLEEP
Bedtime Last Night: _____ : _____
Wake Time This Morning: _____ : _____

MOOD
☺ ☺ ☹

CONNECTION

BREAKFAST

Blueberry-Banana-Nut
Smoothie (p. 46)

LUNCH

Tomato, Peach and Basil Salad
(2 Servings) (p. 176) + 4 oz
Grilled Chicken

DINNER

Pork with Grilled Sweet
Potato Fries (p. 190)

SNACK

½ cup Crunchy
Chickpea Snacks

NOTES TO SELF

WATER

MOVEMENT/WORKOUT Y ☐ N ☐
ACTIVITY: _____

DURATION: _____

INTENSITY: _____

SLEEP

Bedtime Last Night: _____ : _____
Wake Time This Morning: _____ : _____

MOOD

☺ ☺ ☹

CONNECTION

DAY 26

BREAKFAST
Nectarine Bruschetta (p. 168)

LUNCH
Charred Shrimp, Leek and
Asparagus Skewers (p. 178)

DINNER
Harissa Sirloin with Couscous
Salad (p. 192)

SNACK
2 Tbsp Hummus
+ 10 Pita Chips

NOTES TO SELF
_____
_____
_____
_____
_____
_____
_____
_____
_____
_____
_____
_____
_____
_____
_____
_____
_____
_____

WATER

MOVEMENT/WORKOUT Y ☐ N ☐
ACTIVITY: _____
_____
_____
DURATION: _____
_____
INTENSITY: _____
_____
_____

SLEEP
Bedtime Last Night: _____ : _____
Wake Time This Morning: _____ : _____
_____
_____
_____
_____

MOOD
☺ ☺ ☹

_____
_____
_____
_____

CONNECTION
_____
_____
_____
_____
_____

BREAKFAST
Classic Omelet and Greens
(p. 88) + 2 Slices Sprouted
Grain Bread

LUNCH
Chicken Cutlet Sandwiches
(p. 180)

DINNER
Grilled Ratatouille Linguine
(p. 194)

SNACK
Hummus-Stuffed Peppers
(p. 116)

NOTES TO SELF

_____
_____
_____
_____
_____
_____
_____
_____
_____
_____
_____
_____
_____
_____
_____
_____

WATER

MOVEMENT/WORKOUT Y ☐ N ☐
ACTIVITY: _____
_____
_____

DURATION: _____
_____

INTENSITY: _____
_____

SLEEP
Bedtime Last Night: _____ : _____
Wake Time This Morning: _____ : _____

_____
_____
_____

MOOD
☺ ☺ ☹

_____
_____
_____

CONNECTION

_____
_____
_____

DAY 28

BREAKFAST
Strawberry-Almond Oats
(p. 92)

LUNCH
Grilled Eggplant with
Chickpea Croutons (p. 182)
+ Mixed Greens Side Salad
(2 cups Mixed Greens with
2 Tbsp Store-Bought Olive
Oil & Lemon Vinaigrette)

DINNER
Roasted Chicken and Garlic
Potatoes with Red Pepper
Relish (p. 196)

SNACK
1 5.3-oz Container Low-Sugar
Flavored Greek Yogurt

NOTES TO SELF

WATER

MOVEMENT/WORKOUT Y ☐ N ☐
ACTIVITY: _____

DURATION: _____

INTENSITY: _____

SLEEP
Bedtime Last Night: _____ : _____
Wake Time This Morning: _____ : _____

MOOD
☺ 😐 ☹

CONNECTION

WEEK 4

RECIPES

Nectarine Bruschetta

ACTIVE: 5 MIN. ✖ TOTAL: 15 MIN. ✖ SERVES 2

2	Tbsp white wine vinegar
2	tsp honey
1	nectarine, sliced
¼	cup olive oil
½	Tbsp very coarsely cracked black pepper
2	large thick slices country bread
6	Tbsp ricotta cheese, divided

1. In bowl, whisk together vinegar and honey to dissolve. Add nectarine slices and toss to coat; let marinate 10 min. Add olive oil and black pepper and toss to coat.

2. Grill or toast bread and spread with ricotta cheese, then spoon nectarines and juices on top.

About 540 cal, 36 fat (8 g sat), 10 g pro, 400 mg sodtum, 45 g carb, 3 g fiber

Shrimp Bowls with Scallion Vinaigrette

ACTIVE: 30 MIN. ⁘ TOTAL: 30 MIN. ⁘ SERVES 4

- 1½ cups quinoa
- 1 lb broccoli, cut into small florets and stems cut into thin pieces
- 2 Tbsp olive oil, divided
- Kosher salt and pepper
- 20 large peeled and deveined shrimp, tails removed
- 1 Tbsp rice vinegar
- 1 Tbsp finely grated fresh ginger
- 8 oz plum tomatoes, seeds removed and cut into ⅛-in. pieces
- 2 scallions, thinly sliced
- 1 avocado, cut into small pieces

1. Heat oven to 425°F. Heat medium saucepan over medium, add quinoa, and cook, shaking pan occasionally, until lightly toasted, 5 min. Add 3 cups water and immediately cover (it will sputter). Simmer gently for 10 min. Remove from heat, remove lid, cover with a clean towel and let stand 10 min.; fluff with a fork.

2. Meanwhile, on a rimmed baking sheet, toss broccoli with 1 Tbsp oil and ¼ tsp each salt and pepper. Spread in an even layer and roast 15 min. Season shrimp with a pinch each salt and pepper, toss with broccoli and roast until opaque throughout, 6 to 8 min.

3. In medium bowl, whisk together vinegar, ginger and remaining Tbsp oil. Toss with tomatoes, then fold in scallions. Divide quinoa among 4 bowls, then top with shrimp, broccoli and avocado. Spoon tomato-scallion vinaigrette over top.

About 462 cal, 19 g fat (2.5 g sat), 20 g pro, 457 mg sodium, 57 g carb, 12 g fiber

Cucumber and Cantaloupe Quinoa Salad

ACTIVE: 15 MIN. ✂ TOTAL: 50 MIN. ✂ SERVES 4

CUCUMBER AND CANTALOUPE SALAD

½ batch Savory Quinoa Granola

¼ small red onion, sliced

1 Tbsp Champagne vinegar Kosher salt

1 Tbsp olive oil

½ small cantaloupe (about 1½ lbs), cut into 3-in. pieces

1 Persian cucumber, thickly sliced

2 Tbsp fresh mint leaves, torn

½ oz ricotta salata, coarsely grated or shaved

SAVORY QUINOA GRANOLA

½ cup old-fashioned oats

½ cup tricolor quinoa

¼ cup pepitas

2 Tbsp toasted sesame seeds

3 Tbsp honey

2 Tbsp olive oil

1 large egg white Pinch cayenne

¾ tsp salt

Cucumber and Cantaloupe Salad

1. Prepare Savory Quinoa Granola. While it's cooling, in bowl, toss onion with vinegar and ¼ tsp salt and let sit at least 15 min. Stir in olive oil.

2. Arrange cantaloupe and cucumber slices on platter and spoon onion mixture on top. Sprinkle with mint, then granola and ricotta.

Savory Quinoa Granola

1. Heat oven to 325°F. Line rimmed baking sheet with parchment paper or nonstick baking mat.

2. In large bowl, combine oats, quinoa, pepitas and sesame seeds. In small bowl, whisk together honey, oil, egg white, cayenne and salt; drizzle over oat mixture and toss to coat evenly.

3. Spread in even layer into 9- by 8-in. rectangle on prepared baking sheet and bake, stirring twice and reshaping, until golden brown, 20 to 25 min. Let cool completely, then break into pieces.

About 230 cal, 12 g fat (2 g sat), 6 g pro, 335 mg sodium, 28 g carb, 3 g fiber

MAKE IT AHEAD
Store granola in an airtight container at room temp for up to 2 weeks.

Grilled Sweet Potatoes with Lemon-Herb Sauce

ACTIVE: 20 MIN. ✄ TOTAL: 20 MIN. ✄ SERVES 6

½ small red onion, finely chopped
2 tsp grated lemon zest plus ¼ cup juice
2 lbs sweet potatoes, well scrubbed and sliced into ¼-in.-thick rounds
3 Tbsp olive oil, divided, plus more for serving
   Kosher salt and pepper
1 small Fresno chile, seeded and finely chopped
2 Tbsp hempseed (optional)
¼ cup fresh mint, chopped
   Plain Greek yogurt, for serving

1. Heat grill on medium. In small bowl, combine onion and lemon juice. Let sit, tossing occasionally.

2. In large bowl, toss sweet potatoes with 2 Tbsp oil and ¼ tsp each salt and pepper. Grill until slightly charred and tender, 4 to 5 min. per side.

3. Into bowl with onions, stir lemon zest, chile, hemp (if using) and remaining Tbsp oil, then stir in mint. Makes ½ cup relish.

4. Spread Greek yogurt onto platter and drizzle with oil. Arrange sweet potatoes over yogurt and spoon mint relish on top.

About 150 cal, 7 g fat (1 g sat), 2 g pro, 115 mg sodium, 21 g carb, 4 g fiber

LOVE YOUR LEFTOVERS
Refrigerate sweet potatoes and vinaigrette separately in airtight containers for up to 2 days.

Tomato, Peach and Basil Salad

ACTIVE: 10 MIN. ✕ TOTAL: 10 MIN. ✕ SERVES 4

- 1/2 small red onion, thinly sliced
- 1 Tbsp red wine vinegar
- Kosher salt and pepper
- 1 lb heirloom tomatoes
- 1 lb yellow peaches or nectarines
- 2 Tbsp olive oil
- 1/4 cup basil leaves
- 2 oz feta, broken into pieces

1. In small bowl, combine onion and vinegar with ¼ tsp salt. Let sit 5 min.
2. Cut tomatoes and peaches into wedges and arrange on platter.
3. Stir oil into onion mixture and spoon over fruit, then sprinkle with basil, feta and cracked black pepper.

About 75 cal, 4.5 g fat (1 g sat), 2 g pro, 165 mg sodium, 8 g carb, 2 g fiber

Charred Shrimp, Leek and Asparagus Skewers

ACTIVE: 30 MIN. ✂ TOTAL: 30 MIN. ✂ SERVES 4

1 lb (21- to 25-count) peeled and deveined shrimp

1 lb asparagus, trimmed and cut into 2-in. pieces

2 medium leeks, white and light green parts only, cut into ¾-in.-thick rounds

2 Tbsp olive oil
Kosher salt and pepper

2 lemons, halved

½ cup mayonnaise

1½ Tbsp harissa paste

1. Heat grill to medium-high. Thread shrimp, asparagus and leek rounds onto skewers. Brush lightly with oil and season with ½ tsp each salt and pepper.

2. Grill skewers until vegetables are tender and shrimp are opaque throughout, 3 to 4 min. per side.

3. Place lemons on grill alongside skewers, cut sides down, and grill until charred, about 4 min.

4. Into small bowl, squeeze 2 tsp juice from 1 charred lemon half. Stir in mayonnaise and harissa to combine. Serve skewers with harissa mayo and remaining charred lemon halves.

About 370 cal, 28.5 g fat (4.5 g sat), 18 g pro, 1,110 mg sodium, 12 g carb, 2 g fiber

Chicken Cutlet Sandwiches

ACTIVE: 20 MIN. ✖ TOTAL: 20 MIN. ✖ SERVES 4

½ small red onion, thinly sliced

1 Tbsp red wine vinegar
Kosher salt and pepper

1 lb boneless, skinless chicken breasts

1 Tbsp olive oil

6 cups baby spinach

4 5 in. pieces baguette, split and toasted

1. Toss onion with vinegar and ⅛ tsp each salt and pepper; let sit.

2. Cut chicken into 6 thin cutlets. Heat oil in large skillet on medium-high. Season chicken with ½ tsp each salt and pepper and cook until browned and cooked through, 2 min. per side; transfer to cutting board.

3. Add spinach to skillet, season with salt and pepper and cook until just beginning to wilt.

4. Slice chicken and sandwich between baguette halves with spinach and onions.

About 330 cal, 7 g fat (1 g sat), 33 g pro, 705 mg sodium, 32 g carb, 3 g fiber

LOVE YOUR LEFTOVERS
Refrigerate chicken and spinach separately in airtight containers for up to 2 days.

Grilled Eggplant with Chickpea Croutons

ACTIVE: 35 MIN. ⁙ TOTAL: 1 HR. 10 MIN. ⁙ SERVES 4

- 3 Tbsp plus 1 tsp olive oil, divided
- 1 small onion, finely chopped
- 2 cloves garlic, pressed, divided
- Kosher salt
- 1 cup chickpea flour
- 1 Tbsp lemon zest plus 2 tsp lemon juice
- 2 medium eggplants (about 12 oz each)
- ¼ cup plain full fat yogurt
- 1 cup mint leaves, torn
- 2 Tbsp chopped chives

1. Line 4½- by 8½-in. loaf pan with parchment, leaving overhang on two long sides. Heat 1 Tbsp oil in large saucepan on medium. Add onion, 1 garlic clove and ¼ tsp salt and cook, stirring occasionally, until tender, 5 min. Add 2 cups water and bring to a boil. While whisking, slowly stream in chickpea flour and whisk vigorously, off of heat, until mostly lump-free.

2. Transfer mixture to food processor with lemon zest and puree, gradually adding 1 Tbsp oil until completely smooth. Immediately transfer to prepared pan and smooth top. Cover with another piece of parchment and another loaf pan and press with heavy object. Refrigerate until firm, 30 min. to 1 hr.

3. Meanwhile, heat grill to medium-high. Cut chickpea mixture into ½-in. cubes. Heat 1 tsp oil in small skillet and cook in 2 to 3 batches, turning occasionally, until browned, 3 to 5 min. Transfer to paper towel to drain.

4. Slice eggplants lengthwise, ½-in. thick. Brush eggplant slices with remaining Tbsp oil, season with a pinch of salt and grill until tender and lightly charred, about 3 min. per side.

5. In small bowl, whisk together yogurt, lemon juice, remaining garlic and pinch salt. Drizzle yogurt sauce over eggplant and sprinkle with chickpea croutons, mint and chives.

About 255 cal, 13.5 g fat (2 g sat), 8 g pro, 210 mg sodium, 27 g carb, 8 g fiber

Grilled Moroccan Steak and Carrots

ACTIVE: 25 MIN. ✂ TOTAL: 25 MIN. ✂ SERVES 4

1	cup packed cilantro
1	cup packed flat-leaf parsley plus more for serving
1	tsp smoked paprika
1	large clove garlic
½	cup plus 1 Tbsp olive oil
1	tsp lemon zest plus 2 Tbsp lemon juice
	Kosher salt and pepper
1	tsp ground cumin
1	tsp ground coriander
½	tsp ground cinnamon
1½	lbs sirloin steak, cut into 4 pieces
1	lb small carrots, scrubbed, halved lengthwise if thick
1	oz feta, crumbled

1. Heat grill to medium. In blender, puree cilantro, parsley, paprika, garlic, ½ cup oil, lemon zest and juice and ¼ tsp each salt and pepper. Transfer to small bowl.

2. In separate small bowl, combine cumin, coriander and cinnamon with ¼ tsp salt and ½ tsp pepper; rub all over steak. Rub carrots with remaining Tbsp oil and season with ¼ tsp each salt and pepper.

3. Grill steak and carrots, covered, until carrots are tender and steak is medium-rare, 3 to 5 min. per side. Transfer steak to cutting board and let rest 5 min. before slicing.

4. Transfer carrots to platter, drizzle with ¼ cup sauce and sprinkle with feta and parsley. Serve with steak and remaining sauce.

About 635 cal, 46 g fat (11 g sat), 41 g pro, 670 mg sodium, 14 g carb, 5 g fiber

Grilled Leek, Zucchini and Ricotta Pizza

ACTIVE: 35 MIN. ✂ TOTAL: 45 MIN. ✂ SERVES 4

Flour, for surface

1 lb pizza dough

1 large leek, halved lengthwise

2 large zucchini, halved lengthwise

2 Tbsp olive oil
  Kosher salt and pepper

2 tsp finely grated lemon zest plus 3 Tbsp lemon juice

2 cups ricotta cheese
  Mint, for serving

1. Heat oven to 425°F. Line a baking sheet with parchment paper. On a lightly floured surface, shape dough into a large rectangle. Place on prepared sheet and bake 10 min. Remove crust from oven and set aside. Reset oven temp to 475°F.

2. Meanwhile, heat grill on medium-high. Brush leek and zucchini with olive oil; season with salt and pepper. Grill until tender, turning once, 5 to 8 min. Thinly slice vegetables and toss with lemon juice.

3. In a small bowl, mix ricotta with lemon zest and ½ tsp salt. Spread ricotta on crust and top with vegetables. Bake until crust and toppings have browned, 5 to 8 min. Drizzle with olive oil and top with mint if desired.

About 575 cal, 26.5 g fat (11.5 g sat), 22 g pro, 1,235 mg sodium, 60 g carb, 4 g fiber

LOVE YOUR LEFTOVERS
Tightly wrap any leftover pizza and refrigerate for up to 3 days. Warm in oven at 400°F.

Chicken and Asparagus Ribbons with Meyer Lemon Vinaigrette

ACTIVE: 15 MIN. ✂ **TOTAL: 25 MIN.** ✂ **SERVES 4**

1 lb thick asparagus, trimmed
   Kosher salt and pepper
1½ lbs boneless, skinless chicken breasts, cut into 1½-in. pieces
2 Tbsp olive oil, divided
1 Meyer lemon
1 tsp Dijon mustard
¼ cup grated pecorino cheese
5 oz mixed greens
¼ cup roasted almonds, chopped

1. Bring medium pot of water to a boil. Reserve 4 thick spears asparagus, then cut others into 2-in. pieces. Add 1 tsp salt to water, then add asparagus pieces and cook until bright green, about 2 min.; immediately transfer to bowl of ice water to cool. Drain and pat dry.

2. Season chicken with ½ tsp each salt and pepper. Heat 1 Tbsp olive oil in a large skillet on medium-high, add chicken and cook, tossing occasionally, until golden brown on all sides and just cooked through, about 12 min.

3. Into large bowl, grate zest from lemon and squeeze in juice. Whisk in mustard and remaining Tbsp oil, then stir in pecorino.

4. With vegetable peeler, pressing down firmly, create long strips from reserved asparagus. Add to bowl of dressing along with cooked asparagus and toss to coat; fold in chicken, mixed greens and almonds.

About 350 cal, 18 g fat (4 g sat), 41 g pro, 555 mg sodium, 6 g carb, 3 g fiber

Pork with Grilled Sweet Potato Fries

ACTIVE: 30 MIN. ✄ **TOTAL: 30 MIN.** ✄ **SERVES 4**

⅓	cup walnuts
1	small clove garlic
1	small jalapeño, cut up
½	cup mint leaves
1	Tbsp capers
	Kosher salt and pepper
⅓	cup plus 2 Tbsp olive oil
1	Tbsp honey
1	Tbsp fresh lemon juice
3	large sweet potatoes, cut into 1-in. wedges
4	bone-in pork chops (about 1-in.-thick)

1. Heat grill on medium. Make salsa verde: In food processor, finely chop walnuts, garlic, jalapeño, mint, capers and salt. Pulse in honey, lemon juice and ⅓ cup oil.

2. Toss sweet potatoes with 1 Tbsp oil and ¼ tsp each salt and pepper. Brush pork chops with remaining Tbsp oil and season with ¼ tsp each salt and pepper.

3. Grill, covered, until potatoes are tender and the pork is just cooked through, 5 to 7 min. per side. Serve with salsa verde.

About 540 cal, 28.5 g fat (7 g sat), 44 g pro, 440 mg sodium, 26 g carb, 5 g fiber

Harissa Sirloin with Couscous Salad

ACTIVE: 30 MIN. ✄ TOTAL: 35 MIN. ✄ SERVES 4

1	lb small, thin carrots, cut into 2-in. pieces
2	tsp honey
2½	Tbsp olive oil, divided
	Kosher salt and pepper
1	cup couscous
¾	lb beef sirloin steak
1	Tbsp harissa
1	lemon
2	cups baby arugula
½	cup fresh flat-leaf parsley

1. Heat oven to 425°F. On rimmed baking sheet, toss carrots with honey, 1 Tbsp olive oil and ¼ tsp salt and roast until golden brown and tender, 20 to 25 min.

2. Meanwhile, cook couscous per pkg. directions. Heat ½ Tbsp olive oil in large skillet on medium. Pat steak completely dry, season with ¼ tsp each salt and pepper, and cook to desired doneness, 4 to 6 min. per side for medium-rare. Transfer to cutting board, rub with harissa and let rest at least 5 min. before slicing.

3. In large bowl, toss couscous with remaining 1 Tbsp olive oil and zest and juice of lemon. Fold in carrots and sliced steak, then arugula and parsley.

About 445 cal, 20.5 g fat (6 g sat), 22 g pro, 390 mg sodium, 43 g carb, 5 g fiber

Grilled Ratatouille Linguine

ACTIVE: 25 MIN. ✂ TOTAL: 25 MIN. ✂ SERVES 4

12	oz linguine
2	small zucchini, halved lengthwise
1	small eggplant, sliced lengthwise
1	red pepper, halved
1	yellow pepper, halved
1	red onion, cut into rounds
2	Tbsp olive oil
	Kosher salt and pepper
	Grated Parmesan and chopped basil, if desired

1. Heat grill on medium-high. Cook linguine per package directions.

2. Meanwhile, brush zucchini, eggplant, peppers and red onion with oil and season with ½ tsp each salt and pepper.

3. Grill until just tender, 3 to 4 min. per side. Transfer to a cutting board and cut into pieces.

4. Toss linguine with grilled vegetables, drizzling with more oil as desired. Top with grated Parmesan and basil if desired.

About 450 cal, 9.5 g fat (1.5 g sat), 15 g pro, 295 mg sodium, 78 g carb, 7 g fiber

MAKE IT AHEAD
Grill veggies and refrigerate in an airtight container for up to 3 days. Warm and toss with cooked pasta, adding additional oil if the pasta seams dry.

Roasted Chicken and Garlic Potatoes with Red Pepper Relish

ACTIVE: 30 MIN. ✂ TOTAL: 30 MIN. ✂ SERVES 4

1½ lbs golden new potatoes (about 24), halved

4 Tbsp olive oil

4 cloves garlic (2 cloves smashed) Kosher salt and pepper

4 6-oz boneless, skinless chicken breasts

¾ cup roasted red peppers, drained and cut into ⅛-in. pieces

2 scallions, finely chopped

⅓ cup roasted almonds, chopped

3 Tbsp sherry vinegar

2 Tbsp chopped flat-leaf parsley

1. Heat oven to 425°F. On a large rimmed baking sheet, toss potatoes with 2 Tbsp oil. Press 2 cloves garlic over top, sprinkle with ¼ tsp salt, and toss to combine. Roast 15 min.

2. Meanwhile, heat a large skillet on medium-high. Season chicken with ¼ tsp each salt and pepper. Add 1 Tbsp oil to skillet, then add chicken and cook until browned, about 4 min.

3. Turn chicken over, add smashed garlic to skillet and cook 1 min. more. Transfer skillet to oven along with potatoes and roast until chicken is cooked through and potatoes are golden brown and tender, 6 to 8 min. more; transfer chicken and garlic to a cutting board.

4. While chicken cooks, in a bowl, combine peppers, scallions, almonds, vinegar, remaining Tbsp oil and ¼ tsp salt. Chop smashed garlic, add to pepper mixture along with parsley and mix to combine. Serve with chicken and potatoes.

About 520 cal, 23.5 g fat (3.5 g sat), 40 g pro, 590 mg sodium, 38 g carb, 6 g fiber

DATE:

BREAKFAST

_____
_____
_____

LUNCH

_____
_____
_____

DINNER

_____
_____
_____

SNACKS

_____
_____
_____

NOTES TO SELF

_____
_____
_____
_____
_____
_____
_____
_____
_____
_____

WATER

MOVEMENT/WORKOUT Y ☐ N ☐
ACTIVITY: _____
_____

DURATION: _____
_____

INTENSITY: _____
_____

SLEEP
Bedtime Last Night: _____ : _____
Wake Time This Morning: _____ : _____
_____
_____
_____

MOOD

☺ ☺ ☹
_____
_____
_____
_____

CONNECTION
_____
_____
_____
_____
_____

DATE:

BREAKFAST
_____
_____
_____

LUNCH
_____
_____
_____

DINNER
_____
_____
_____

SNACKS
_____
_____
_____

NOTES TO SELF
_____
_____
_____
_____
_____
_____
_____
_____
_____
_____
_____
_____

WATER

MOVEMENT/WORKOUT Y ☐ N ☐
ACTIVITY: _____
_____

DURATION: _____
_____

INTENSITY: _____
_____
_____

SLEEP
Bedtime Last Night: _____ : _____
Wake Time This Morning: _____ : _____
_____
_____
_____

MOOD
☺ 😐 ☹
_____
_____
_____

CONNECTION
_____
_____
_____
_____

DATE:

BREAKFAST

_____
_____
_____

LUNCH

_____
_____
_____

DINNER

_____
_____
_____

SNACKS

_____
_____
_____

NOTES TO SELF

_____
_____
_____
_____
_____
_____
_____
_____
_____
_____
_____

WATER

☐ ☐ ☐ ☐ ☐ ☐ ☐ ☐

MOVEMENT/WORKOUT Y ☐ N ☐
ACTIVITY: _____
_____
_____

DURATION: _____
_____

INTENSITY: _____
_____
_____

SLEEP
Bedtime Last Night: _____ : _____
Wake Time This Morning: _____ : _____
_____
_____
_____

MOOD
☺ ☻ ☹
_____
_____
_____
_____

CONNECTION
_____
_____
_____
_____

DATE:

BREAKFAST

_____
_____
_____

LUNCH

_____
_____
_____

DINNER

_____
_____
_____

SNACKS

_____
_____
_____

NOTES TO SELF

_____
_____
_____
_____
_____
_____
_____
_____
_____
_____
_____

WATER

☐ ☐ ☐ ☐ ☐ ☐ ☐ ☐

MOVEMENT/WORKOUT Y ☐ N ☐
ACTIVITY: _____
_____

DURATION: _____

INTENSITY: _____
_____

SLEEP
Bedtime Last Night: _____ : _____
Wake Time This Morning: _____ : _____
_____
_____
_____

MOOD
😊 😐 ☹
_____
_____
_____

CONNECTION
_____
_____
_____
_____

DATE:

BREAKFAST

_____
_____
_____

LUNCH

_____
_____
_____

DINNER

_____
_____
_____

SNACKS

_____
_____
_____

NOTES TO SELF

_____
_____
_____
_____
_____
_____
_____
_____
_____
_____
_____

WATER

🥛 🥛 🥛 🥛 🥛 🥛 🥛 🥛

MOVEMENT/WORKOUT Y ☐ N ☐
ACTIVITY: _____
_____

DURATION: _____

INTENSITY: _____
_____

SLEEP
Bedtime Last Night: _____ : _____
Wake Time This Morning: _____ : _____
_____
_____

MOOD
🙂 😐 🙁
_____
_____
_____
_____

CONNECTION
_____
_____
_____
_____

DATE:

BREAKFAST
_____
_____
_____

LUNCH
_____
_____
_____

DINNER
_____
_____
_____

SNACKS
_____
_____
_____

NOTES TO SELF
_____
_____
_____
_____
_____
_____
_____
_____
_____
_____

WATER

MOVEMENT/WORKOUT Y ☐ N ☐
ACTIVITY: _____
_____
DURATION: _____
_____
INTENSITY: _____
_____

SLEEP
Bedtime Last Night: _____ : _____
Wake Time This Morning: _____ : _____
_____
_____
_____

MOOD
☺ 😐 ☹
_____
_____
_____
_____

CONNECTION
_____
_____
_____
_____
_____

DATE:

BREAKFAST
_____
_____
_____

LUNCH
_____
_____
_____

DINNER
_____
_____
_____

SNACKS
_____
_____
_____

NOTES TO SELF
_____
_____
_____
_____
_____
_____
_____
_____
_____
_____

WATER

MOVEMENT/WORKOUT Y ☐ N ☐
ACTIVITY: _____
_____

DURATION: _____
_____

INTENSITY: _____
_____

SLEEP
Bedtime Last Night: _____ : _____
Wake Time This Morning: _____ : _____
_____
_____
_____

MOOD
☺ 😐 ☹
_____
_____
_____

CONNECTION
_____
_____
_____

DATE:

BREAKFAST
_____
_____
_____

LUNCH
_____
_____
_____

DINNER
_____
_____
_____

SNACKS
_____
_____
_____

NOTES TO SELF
_____
_____
_____
_____
_____
_____
_____
_____
_____
_____

WATER

☐ ☐ ☐ ☐ ☐ ☐ ☐ ☐

MOVEMENT/WORKOUT Y ☐ N ☐
ACTIVITY: _____
_____

DURATION: _____
_____

INTENSITY: _____
_____

SLEEP
Bedtime Last Night: _____ : _____
Wake Time This Morning: _____ : _____
_____
_____
_____

MOOD
☺ ☺ ☹
_____
_____
_____

CONNECTION
_____
_____
_____

DATE:

BREAKFAST

_____
_____
_____

LUNCH

_____
_____
_____

DINNER

_____
_____
_____

SNACKS

_____
_____
_____

NOTES TO SELF

_____
_____
_____
_____
_____
_____
_____
_____
_____
_____
_____

WATER

☐ ☐ ☐ ☐ ☐ ☐ ☐ ☐

MOVEMENT/WORKOUT Y ☐ N ☐
ACTIVITY: _____
_____

DURATION: _____
_____

INTENSITY: _____
_____

SLEEP
Bedtime Last Night: _____ : _____
Wake Time This Morning: _____ : _____
_____
_____
_____

MOOD
☺ ☺ ☹
_____
_____
_____
_____

CONNECTION
_____
_____
_____
_____

DATE:

BREAKFAST

_____
_____
_____
_____

LUNCH

_____
_____
_____

DINNER

_____
_____
_____

SNACKS

_____
_____
_____

NOTES TO SELF

_____
_____
_____
_____
_____
_____
_____
_____
_____
_____
_____

WATER

MOVEMENT/WORKOUT Y ☐ N ☐
ACTIVITY: _____
_____

DURATION: _____
_____

INTENSITY: _____
_____

SLEEP
Bedtime Last Night: _____ : _____
Wake Time This Morning: _____ : _____
_____
_____
_____

MOOD

☺ ☹ ☹
_____
_____
_____
_____

CONNECTION
_____
_____
_____
_____

Thank You

FOR PURCHASING THE GOOD HOUSEKEEPING
28-DAY MEDITERRANEAN DIET BOOK.

We hope you have a happy and healthy year.
If you'd like to expand your *Good Housekeeping* library with
cookbooks, meal plans and more, visit our store at
Shop.GoodHousekeeping.com

HEARST